THE MENTAL

Bobbie Hanvey

WONDERLAND PRESS
Belfast

Published in Great Britain by WONDERLAND PRESS 1996

WONDERLAND PRESS is an imprint of
Wonderland Promotions Ltd. Belfast BT9 5JQ

A catalogue record for this book is
available from the British Library
ISBN 0 9529439 0 5

Printed and bound in Great Britain by
Guernsey Press Co Ltd
Guernsey, Channel isles
Tel: (01481) 45866

CONTENTS

THE FIRST DAY

THE INTERVIEW

BARNEY AND THE RUSSIANS

FISTY'S LESSON

THE NEWS OF THE WORLD

SING ME SOME BOB DYLAN

THE RAILWAY STATION

JANUARY 1967

EASTER

THE DAY TRIP

STILL ON THE BUS

THE BIG HOTEL

COMING HOME

THE ARRANGEMENT

MONTANA MORIARTY

THE CANTEEN

BILLY AND THE HOLY SISTERS

THE BLOTTER FOR HER EYES

THE VISITOR

THAT STORMY NIGHT

THE DREAM

EPILOGUE: WHERE ARE YOU GOING SIR?

'THE FIRST DAY'

At 6.40 am on the morning of the 4th December 1966, I knocked three times on the thick, grey office door of Senior Nursing Officer, Mick O'Reilly.

That door was solid!

In fact, it was so solid I wondered how my feeble tapping, loud and energetic as it sounded to me, could ever make its way through and be heard on the other side.

This was not the kind of door you meet every day; this was not the one you pushed or pulled, as directed by neat little name plates, at eye level, and had forgotten about the second it let you through. This was the real thing, and caused me to realise that for years I had been opening and closing fakes; just hollow, stupid rectangles of swinging cardboard.

'Good morning, Nurse Hanvey,' he smiled as he opened the door at last. 'You're very welcome.'

'Thank you, Mr O'Reilly, and good morning to you too, Sir,' I replied.

'The first thing we do at Downshire, before we begin work, Nurse Hanvey, is to have a good hearty breakfast in the Staff Canteen. The canteen's this way,' he pointed, as we started walking.

Within minutes, we had sat down to grapefruit, cornflakes and the best bacon and egg I had ever tasted. A full pot of tea, complete with a cosy, sat on the table between us. (This, remember, was in the days just before the dusty tea bag was to become popular).

Walking briskly, through what seemed to be endless corridors, the dull echo of our feet thumped in time to my heartbeat; our voices suddenly amplified, and then were normal again, as ceilings became higher and lower at various points along the way.

Mr O'Reilly held two massive keys in his right hand, which could open every door in the hospital. I held mine tightly, yet I had still to open my first lock.

Today, I would begin work in Male Finneston House Ambulant, which held fifty psychogeriatric patients, suffering from senile dementia, and the problems associated with old age.

This building was separate from the Main Hospital, and had been opened in 1955 to relieve the overcrowding taking place at that time. Housing both male and female units, these wards could hold up to one hundred and eighty patients.

Passing the 'Sugar Bowl' where nurses and patients would socialise and drink tea, but not at such an unearthly hour of the morning as this, Mr O'Reilly informed me it was built of cedarwood, and at a cost of over eight thousand pounds, earlier that same year of 1966.

The 'Old' Sugar Bowl opened in 1959 in what was originally a mortuary and later a paint store, was totally inadequate in meeting the needs of a rising patient population.

As well polished shoes crunched on crackling ice, warm breath cut the chilly stillness, and our lungs experienced a clinical freshness which wouldn't last for long.

The universal trademark of a Mental Nurse, the long white coat, felt new and awkward. Stiff with starch, it had a mind all of its own, and moved persistently from side to side, in total opposition to my own body movements.

My badge read, 'B. Hanvey, Student Nurse', and I was so proud of that.

Within minutes, we had passed through the green gate in the ivy covered perimeter wall, crossed the main Ardglass to Downpatrick Road, and were standing on the slippery doorstep of Finneston House. I was terrified, but kept it to myself.

2

'Nurse Hanvey, when you open the door of a locked ward you close it firmly behind you, and lock it again. Now, Nurse, would you like to open your first door?'

'Yes, I would, Mr O'Reilly.'

My hand was shaking with anticipation as the brand new silver key stubbornly refused to go between my finger and thumb. I tried to concentrate and apply pressure, but it wouldn't work.

It wasn't opening the door which bothered me, but having spent the previous three days in the safe confines of the Nurses' Home my brain was saturated to bursting point with stories of madness, post mortems and suicides, gleefully recounted by other members of the junior nursing staff, and all for my benefit. Some benefit!

My mind was running so fast I could hear it tick, and this new world which I'd never seen before was now only inches away.

Mr. O'Reilly must have encountered people like me before who stalled at the first fence, because he made reference to the freezing cold of that morning, and how difficult it must be to use a key with fingers which were 'turning into ice by the second'.

'Click'. I'd done it.

We were now in the ward, with the door locked tightly behind us. This was to be my place of work for the next month, and the first thing which struck me was the nose-burning smell of fifty incontinent patients. It was so bad it almost had me taking a backward step.

Urine soaked sheets of twisted 'rope' were tangled around old limbs, both active and still. Farts of differing tones echoed everywhere; Mr. O'Reilly shook his head and told me this was 'The Dawn Chorus'. The floor was flat and long like a football field in winter, with scores of reflective puddles of pungent pish, scattered randomly, but still with enough dry ground left for walking on without getting my shoes wet.

Mr O'Reilly explained that 'smart' patients would get out of their beds in the middle of the night and make their water on the floor. I thought a move such as this was even more than clever.

Voices full of venom and volume, as if possessed, unashamedly roared and screamed; whispered, whined, mimicked, moaned and distorted ..... 'Dirty rotten bastard'; 'Your fuckin' arse is stinking'; 'Your mother's a hoor' and 'Shove it up your cunt', quickly shocked me into this new reality, as they reverberated from the bed posts at difficult to determine locations within the ward.

Mr O'Reilly, who was a genuinely religious man, and a daily Communicant, looked at me in a sympathetic, almost apologetic way, obviously embarrassed by the strong language. I felt it was now my turn to repay an earlier favour, and this time came to his rescue.
'It's alright, Sir, sure they probably don't even realise what they're saying.'

'Indeed they don't, indeed they don't. Nurse Hanvey, if you manage to come through today, you'll make a great nurse.'

I nodded, but in disbelief.

I wanted to pull off my white coat, dump it in one of the puddles and head straight back to County Fermanagh. But I then realised Fermanagh had nothing to offer me. I had left it; in fact, I had left it twice.

I could make 'phone calls to anywhere, from that cold, red box beside the old police barracks in Brookeborough's Main Street, just to hear a different accent, and I constantly believed that escape from a place such as that couldn't be all that difficult, if I put my mind to it.

Still, I would give this nursing game another half an hour and see what happened, but at the same time it seemed like I was already admitting defeat and very soon things were to become much worse as Mr O'Reilly led me in the direction of the bed nearest the door.

It was exactly now 7.25 am on 4th December 1966; time for my baptism of fire.

Stainless steel trolleys loaded high with fresh sheets, towels, blankets and disinfectant edged slowly yet methodically across the ward, transforming the haze of the previous nine hours into instant freshness once again.

4

Busy bodies were on the march - scores of them - doing what they had done sixty years ago, only doing it all over again.

Some were wearing those old Ebenezer style night shirts, which ended just below the knee, whilst others were as naked as the day they were born.

They were heading to the 'churches and offices', to the 'farms and factories' and to the 'golf clubs and restaurants'. On their way, they would stop momentarily to gaze on their own reflections in countless windows. Then as the outside darkness slowly gave way, the winter's sun quietly wiped their images from each and every pane.
All strands of society were here. There was no class distinction now. Eighty year olds with erections and masturbating. Was this hell, or was life really supposed to be like this? At the time I wasn't so sure; now I have no doubts whatsoever.

We had now arrived at the bed beside the door.

Every sheet and every blanket was covered in thick, brown shite.

'Sticks like shite to a blanket,' I thought.

These bed clothes which had been spotlessly clean the night before, now hung sadly over the edge of the bare, spongy mattress and trailed haphazardly onto the floor. Long, straggly, nicotine-coloured map-like shapes embellished the white sheets, and when viewed from different angles resembled complicated works of art. The overpowering caustic smell of strong, stale pish, hung in the immediate area, and was almost visible, like a sulphur cloud.

My breakfast was still where I put it over an hour ago, but how long it would stay there I simply didn't know. I retched and retched, and at the same time tried to keep a stiff upper lip.

Mr O'Reilly now told me the patient's name.

He was Paddy.

Paddy's eyes were the maddest I'd ever seen.

A fixed, floating stare ended somewhere three feet above me, as his head moved up and down, and from side to side, but all the time still gazing on the same spot.

Being the new naive nurse that I was, I raised my eyes to see what he was looking at, and Mr O'Reilly who was watching me laughed softly, 'Did you see it too, Nurse Hanvey?'

I smiled back at him, trying hard not to laugh, and replied, 'I think I just missed it, Sir.'

Tightening his lips he nodded, obviously appreciating my answer, and for me the ice had now been broken.

Paddy's eyes were wide and frightened, as if being constantly driven by millions of demons.

His scarce skin stretched tightly across sharp bones, in Belsen-like pose.

From head to foot he was smothered in a brown caked shell and his mouth, which revealed two rows of perfectly healthy teeth, was overflowing with the stuff.

Here I was, with a mouth of poor teeth, and no shite. Wasn't the world ill divided!

His hands were also full, and he was eating it.

'My God; how did he manage to end up like this?' I thought.

With legs pulled chestwards in the foetal position, he picked more from his arse and kept on eating, his facial expression, forever changing, from maniac laughter to sad bewilderment.

I was getting scared again, and wondered what I was doing here.

They had never mentioned this in the Hospital Brochure. Ah, well, perhaps they simply hadn't room.

I had been thrown in at the deep end. But within six years, I would also become an old hand, observing the new student nurses, with their faces of shock and disbelief, and hoping that they, too, would 'make it'.

'THE INTERVIEW'

Before applying to Downshire I had already attended an interview in the Tyrone and Fermanagh Mental Hospital in Omagh, which was only twenty miles from my home in Brookeborough.

I later discovered when reading a book on interviews that the one I'd had there had been of the 'panel' type, where five or six people constantly threw questions at me.

'Why are the Americans in Vietnam?' asked one.

'Vietnam is divided into North and South. Which side do the Americans support?' asked another.

'Which side are the Russians on?'

'Where is Cambodia?'

'Who are the Viet Cong?'

At that stage of my life, and in spite of all the bad things the Russians had done on 'my' religion, not to mention the unspeakable horrors they had bestowed on my hero, Cardinal Mindszenty, for some strange reason completely unknown to me I was now solidly behind the 'comrades', and was as red as they were.

For years I would try to remember who it was who brainwashed me into thinking like that, but my mind has always remained a blank.

'Mr Hanvey,' said a snipey nosed ould doll, dressed up in a new outfit, 'Why do you dislike Americans?'

'Just,' I replied, and left it like that. I wondered, if I happened to pass the interview, which was highly unlikely, would they train me as a psychiatric nurse, or send me on an extended tour of duty with the B-Specials in Vietnam?

Vietnam. They were Vietnam on the brain, and that snipey ould doll asking all the hard questions had more paint on her than the Titanic. My father used to tell me there was only one thing in this life worse than an ould doll and that was a painted ould doll.

This one had never been born: she had been launched, and had the track of the champagne bottle on her face to prove it.

A week later, two letters slapped into the hallway of my home. One was from Omagh, and informed me that my interview 'for the position of Student Nurse' had, on this occasion, been unsuccessful. The other one had a Downpatrick postmark and brought the good news of my coming interview at Downshire.

Deciding I wasn't going to make the same mistake twice I took the bus to Enniskillen and bought a book on interviews, which told me everything I thought I needed to know.

It told me how to sit; how to maintain eye contact, although I never had a problem with that; how to dress; never to fidget; never to volunteer information and always to give short answers. It also explained the different types of interviews I was likely to encounter; the panel, the one-to-one and so on, with black drawings of people and tables and an empty chair for me to sit on, to help create the mood.

So when the bus finally stopped in Downpatrick's Market Street on that dark, rainy afternoon in 1966, I said to myself, 'This is it!' In reality, it was one of the most foul, ignorant days I had ever seen. Vicious and unimaginative, was how I'll always remember it, with most of whatever light there was, and there wasn't much, being splashed in my direction from a row of bleak, yellow shop windows.

People stood huddled in doorways, in bunches, hoping for a break in the deluge, but at the same time standing with still, expressionless faces, as if waiting for a funeral to pass them. Anyone who did brave the elements did so with head down, collar up, and with frozen hands buried deep in wet, uncomfortable pockets. Sightseeing was well and truly out of the question.

Crossing the street to ask for directions to Downshire Hospital, I felt a sharp tug on the back of my overcoat.

9

'Jesus Christ! You scared the fuck out of me. What's wrong?' I asked, as I quickly turned and faced him.

This guy was a 'stranger spotter' by profession, and he was right first time.

'Could you spare a few bob for an ould drink?' he smiled.

'I'm afraid not, I have no job, no money, so I'm in the same boat as yourself.'

'And what boat would that be Sir,' he sneered sarcastically.

'The Titanic,' I answered.

'Aw, fuck you, you smart bastard, and the horse you rode in on,' he snapped, as he wheeled round and headed into the rain.

'And fuck you too,' I shouted; 'your mother musta fucked a midget to have ended up with a wee cunt like you.' It was not until some minutes later that I realised he probably could have killed me.

During my schooldays I loved to fight and would have faced anyone, big or small, regardless of the consequences. But it had been almost seven years since my knuckles had 'landed', and I felt I had, for a long time now, become too civilised. A dangerous condition to adopt in a mad, bad old world such as this.

A small lady in her fifties, laden down with two massive bags of groceries came straight towards me. She had probably walked this footpath every day of her life and wasn't moving over for man, woman or child. This was her turf.

'Excuse me, could you tell me the way to Downshire Hospital, please?' I asked.

'Oh, you'd be lookin' for The Mental. Do you see that road?' she pointed, after dropping one of her bags beside a clump of freshly cut Christmas trees.

'I do,' I nodded in total agreement.

'Well, keep following that road for a mile or so, and when you get that far you'll be almost there, and you could always ask somebody else. I'm glad it's you who's goin' there and not me,' she laughed. 'I don't mind going there, but if they let me out when I arrive then that's when I'll start worrying,' I smiled.

She immediately stopped laughing, gave me a strange, vacant look and waddled off into the rapidly falling darkness, glancing over her shoulder at regular intervals, to ensure I was heading in the opposite direction.

Walking through the main gates of Downshire Hospital I followed the road which swept slowly to the right, climbing slightly up-hill, every step providing me with a wider view of the biggest, most awesome building I'd ever seen.

Dozens of ancient beech trees helped to reduce the looming menace which overwhelmed me more with every passing second.

The windows, and there seemed to be millions of them, hung like lonely picture frames, but all complete with silent, distant faces.

Seated in the Chief Male Nurse's Office, I couldn't help but notice the big, matt black telephone which looked like it weighed a ton.

Mr Lees was a tall man. Even when seated, he towered over me, as I sat on the other side of his dark, shiny desk. His black three-piece suit with matching tie neatly knotted between the whitest starched collar imaginable, immediately made me feel shabby, even though I thought I'd dressed up as best I could for an occasion such as this.

'Mr Lees, Sir,' I began, 'I left school at fifteen.' (Oh God I'd just volunteered information and the book warned me not to impart any).

'So did I, son; don't worry about it,' he reassured me. 'I hear you play the guitar and sing.'

'Yes, Sir, I do indeed. I play on the radio. The B.B.C.'

'I heard that,' he murmured, and then proceeded to tell me that music and song was becoming a very important part of his new programme at Downshire, and was most therapeutic for the patients.

'From next week,' he went on, 'The Christmas Ward Parties will begin and continue right up to the New Year. If you like you can start work in a few days time on December the fourth, and you will be given time off work, in the afternoons and at night, to entertain the patients. Would you like the job?'

I was thunder struck!

I didn't know what to expect on the wards or what might await me, but I didn't care. I simply couldn't believe my luck. Imagine reading that book on interviews three times, and all for nothing: what a waste of time!

But still Mr Lees, in his soft, rich, Scots burr had just elevated my station in life to that of Student Nurse, which had been, for some time now, my main ambition in this world.

I shook his hand and said, 'Thank you very much, Mr Lees. You have made me very happy, and I won't let you down.'

'I don't believe you will, Nurse Hanvey, I don't believe you will.'

'Jesus, he's just called me Nurse Hanvey,' and I hadn't even taken the Oath of Allegiance to Her Majesty, Queen Elizabeth yet. But since she was going to pay my bills I would have no doubts in that direction, and I was sure Cardinal Mindszenty would have no objections either.

Before leaving the room, I shook his hand, again, and thanked him once more, and headed off to celebrate with a cup of tea.

Going along the lofty corridors, I felt so elated I gave the loudest, happiest cheer of my life.

Two old patients who were passing by started laughing, and assuming I was one of them, began running and shouting at the top of their voices; 'He's mad!, he's mad!!, he's mad!!! He's fuckin' mad! The cunt's mad! They should lock him fuckin' up.'

At the top of the steps outside the pharmacy I sat down and laughed until my sides were sore, but finally realised I'd better stop it, before someone did really lock me up.

In the canteen, I fell into line with the rest of the nurses queuing for tea, and my career in nursing had finally begun.

'BARNEY AND THE RUSSIANS'

It was 1954, in the days when the Cold War raged between East and West, and where most walls, in most houses, had layer upon layer of glossy brown paint at least somewhere on some of them.

My Primary School Master was a tall, kind man with a long nose which always dripped, and his large white handkerchief which was in constant use, but more often in winter, spent little or no time in his pocket.

His heavy brown-rimmed spectacles were mostly used for gazing over, rather than for reading. They had the desired effect of warning us of worse to come and of subduing us in the meantime until 'it' finally arrived, which was usually in the shape of the dull, yellow cane with split tip, which hung on a six inch nail, beside the blackboard. His name was Barney McCusker.

Now and again, but not very often, the Master would mesmerise us with stories of the Russian Heathens who could invade Northern Ireland at any given moment.

'They would only come in winter,' he said, 'because those white faced pagans had never seen a decent summer in their miserable lives. God's sun could never be seen to shine on such people; they are the scum of the earth.'

After a lunch of jam sandwiches and a third of a pint of cold milk, the Master asked us to form a line around the room, with our backs to the wall.

During the nineteen twenties he had been interned on the prison ship Argenta, as a suspected member of the Irish Republican Army. We were never able to prove this, but the fact that he had 'done some time' for Ireland, gave him a certain mystical standing in his own community.

His not too infrequent drinking sprees, in Jim O'Donnell's pub, were put down to the 'torture he must have endured at the hands of the British', and as far as the Catholic people of the village were concerned, he was one of them, and had long since been forgiven for his little weakness.

Knocking flies from the air in mid-flight, with the accuracy of an army marksman, his well-seasoned, bendy cane, swished its burning message home, time after time.

With our backs now to the wall, and in much the same way as a General might inspect his troops, he walked up and down in front of us, his left thumb stretching the elastic of his braces out in front of him, until we thought it must surely break. Then, with cane resting easily on his broad right shoulder, in rifle fashion, he shouted, 'Collins!'

'Yes, Sir.'

'Collins, could you imagine the Russian hordes approaching the village of Brookeborough from three directions; from Fivemiletown, from Maguiresbridge and from Lisnaskea; not by the tens, not by the hundreds, but by the thousands, and not so much as one pair of God's holy rosary beads between them? Can you imagine that, Collins?'

As bewildered as the rest of us, Collins replied in a low, soft voice, 'Yes, Sir.'

'I can't hear you, Collins. Did you hear him boys?'

Twenty boys replied with one voice, 'No, Sir.'

'Collins?'

Collins took a deep breath and roared in full voice, 'Yes, Sir.'

'Now, having successfully imagined that, young Collins, could you once again also imagine why these Godless creatures would want to come to Northern Ireland in the first place?'

'No, Sir,' replied Collins.

'Breen, do you think they would be coming here on their holidays?'

'No, I don't, Sir.'
'Green, do you think they would be coming to do some fishing in the Colebrooke River, and maybe when they're at it, call in with Sir Basil Brooke, for a cup of tea and biscuits?'

'I don't know, Sir.'

'Maguire?'

No answer.

'Maguire, are you sleeping on your feet?'

'I don't know, Sir.'

Everybody laughed - except Maguire.

'Well, boys, I'll tell you why they would want to come into our midst, and most certainly come they will, if they're given half a chance. Ireland is a Catholic country, the greatest Catholic country in the world, and the one thing which these Communist heathens hate more than Catholics is God Himself. God, Himself! Did you all hear that boys?'

The whole class replied in unison, 'Yes, Sir. God Himself.'

'Back in Russia, priests say Mass on the run.'

'Jesus, that's some trick,' I thought, 'saying Mass and running at the same time.'

'Bishops, priests and Cardinals are locked up in the dungeons of dark, cold prisons and are never let out. Right now, as I speak to you, one of the holiest Catholic men in the world is being tortured and spat upon by these fiends.

'Boys, I never want you to forget the name of that brave Catholic man, who at this very moment is suffering for his faith, and is suffering for you. He comes from the country of Hungary, boys, and his name is one of the greatest names which you'll ever hear in your entire lifetimes: Cardinal Mindszenty.

'Catholics in Russia who are found with rosary beads, holy statues, prayer books or any religious objects are dragged from their beds in the middle of the night; from the oldest grandmother to the youngest child in the cot, they are lined up outside their homes, in the freezing snow, and shot like dogs.

'Now, Collins, tell me this.

'What would you do, if the Russians came to your house in the middle of the night, in the middle of winter, and asked you what your religion was?'

'I'd tell them I was a Protestant, Sir,' Collins replied confidently.

I didn't know what the right answer was, but I knew this wasn't it.

The cane had now taken up a new, more threatening position.

'Hold out your hand, Collins; right or left; the choice is entirely yours.'

He held out his right hand and pulled it back again, and then advanced the left.

Collins gritted his teeth so hard his eyes automatically closed at the same time; his face livid; grinning the grin of all the pain in the world, and he hadn't even been slapped yet.

Two of the best, landed in quick succession, and the inevitable rubbing of hands took place, in the hope that the hurt could be more evenly dispersed to other unaffected regions.

'Collins, Protestants believe in the same God as you and I, so after they had murdered all the Catholics, Collins, what would they then do?'

17

Collins scratched his chin; his eyes fixed on an invisible point on the ceiling.

'They would then murder all the Protestants, Sir.'

'Correct. Now you are beginning to think, Collins.'

Collins smiled one of his big happy smiles, and the slaps he had just received, minutes earlier, were now long forgotten.

'Flanagan, what would you tell them your religion was?'
'I wouldn't tell them anything, Sir, I'd go for the police.'

'Did you hear that clearly, boys?

'Collins is busy telling them he is a Protestant, and now Flanagan, who is surrounded by army lorries and tanks, and twenty thousand Russian soldiers, all heavily armed to the teeth, has the gumption to try and make us believe he'd simply walk down the Main Street in Brookeborough to the barracks and get the police.

'God help Ireland, and protect the lot of us, from the likes of people like Flanagan,' he laughed.

'Donnelly do you believe that an R.U.C. Sergeant and five brave young Constables armed with old rusty .303 rifles, would stand much of a chance against such a well armed gang of heathens?'

'No chance, Sir.'

'As much as I hate to say it, and to even have to admit it, Donnelly, you're right; those young officers wouldn't stand a dog's chance.

'Murphy?'

'I would tell them I was a Catholic Sir, and that I was prepared to die for my Faith, and that's what I'd tell them, so I would.'

'Correct, Murphy. Well done. You'd tell them you were a Catholic, and you wouldn't care if they shot you or not; you would tell them you were prepared to die for your Faith.'

The message was now crystal clear, and I suppose that that single, simple story did more to broaden my mind than any other experience in life.

How could we Catholic children, taught so well by old Barney McCusker, grow up to hate B-men and Protestants, when the upper-most worry in our minds was an imminent Russian invasion?

The Protestants in this part of Fermanagh, at any rate, would have no problems from the class of Saint Mary's, 1950. It was super psychology at its best, and I often wondered if the Master was the genius behind such a scheme of outstanding brilliance, or if the C.I.A. and the Vatican had worked it out between them.

Somehow, I tended to believe that old Barney was the architect.

Years later, when attending the Technical School in Enniskillen, I sent away for 'The Soviet Weekly'. It was a dull, boring newspaper, which informed us of the tonnage of grain produced annually, and how the brave Russian troops had spotted the Chinese who were watching their borders.

We were afraid of the Russians, the Russians in turn were afraid of the Chinese, and just about everybody in the world was afraid of somebody else.

For years afterwards I believed the Russians to be devious, crafty bastards, for the simple reason their publication, 'The Soviet Weekly' was printed in London, at the most unusual address; 'Rosary Gardens'.

'FISTY'S LESSON'

Fisty always drank at that table.

He held court there, gave advice to anyone who asked for it and, much to the annoyance of local people, insisted on keeping the joker in the pack when playing cards. He said the joker could be a two of diamonds, a King, a Queen or an Ace; it could be anything you wanted it to be. In fact, it could be a great card, if it ever showed up in your 'hand'. All the card men in the village at the time believed it was the devil's card, but if it showed up on occasions to strengthen their game they were then prepared to overlook such a sinister addition. My father told me that if I ever ventured to play cards and tried to use the joker, the club foot of old Satan could well appear below the table. Not being brave enough to test the validity of such old warnings, I never used that card. In fact to this very day I'm still afraid of it.

The back room of Jim O'Donnell's pub in Brookeborough was Fisty's 'office'. I was fifteen at the time.

Extremely handsome, with perfect, pearly teeth and well trimmed moustache, he had that Errol Flynn swashbuckling look about him which always commanded attention. But the first thing which I always looked out for was the big, rusty hook which peeped out from the wide, well-worn, oily cuff of his overcoat.

It was said he was a 'woman's man'.

He told me he'd been to every country in the world twice, and I believed him. I had no reason to do otherwise.

He had hunted the Abominable Snowman in the Himalayas, captured two Russian spies in Moscow for the Americans, courted the Dalai Lama's wife and her sister at the same time, and had the 'phone number for Scotland Yard. His last piece of information was credible, because in those grey days of the late nineteen fifties the best known 'phone number in the British Isles must have been Whitehall 1212.

Every night, just before the news ended, the announcer would ask us to dial that number if we happened to encounter some gangster or criminal who was running from the law. Anyway, none of them ever bothered to show up in Brookeborough, so I never got the opportunity of ringing that number, but I felt it was useful to have, just the same.

At some point in his lifetime, Fisty must have experienced a real frightener with women, because he would scare me to death with hair raising stories about the fairer sex.

The stories were quite bizarre, though they became less so, on reflection, as I grew older. Yet to a young, gullible country boy of fifteen they were quite believable.

'Always be careful with the 'fannies', Bobbie,' said Fisty; 'Never trust them, and always check them out with your fingers first, because in the dense, steaming jungles of the Amazon, where I worked, the men fitted their women's fannies with teeth!'

'Christ! A vicious circle, a fanny with teeth,' he roared, thumping the table once with his hook.

'Oh my good God, a vicious circle, a fanny with teeth,' I cringed.

'Go on, Fisty, tell me more,' I asked, as I felt I needed to further my education.

'Well, son, it's like this. Here in Northern Ireland it's a well known fact that most of the adult population who look after their teeth have thirty-two. Ireland has thirty-two counties and the people who live there have thirty-two teeth. It's a plain, simple mathematical fact!'

'Fuck, he's brainy,' I thought.

'But, young Hanvey, in the darkest Amazon, where coffee grows on hedges, and where trees are ten times, even twenty times higher than the spire of Brookeborough Chapel, and where those very same trees are so close together the people living there, never see the sun; how many teeth do you think those natives have in their heads? Ten; twenty; thirty-two; forty?'

21

'Thirty-two,' I answered.

'You're almost right,' said Fisty. 'Twenty-eight. They have only twenty-eight. So where did the other four go?'
'I don't know.'

'Well, it's like this, young Hanvey, and when you study it, it's really very simple. As you know, we Ulster folk are known all over the world as being the wisest people on the face of this earth, and being so wise, God bestowed us with wisdom teeth; the exact teeth that prove we have wisdom and are wise. Do you follow me so far?'

'I do.'

'Now, here's where we differ. Most people in the Amazon jungles still do not believe in God. I managed to convert a few when I was out there, but not enough to create any impression. To date, their wisdom of God is zero, and that, my friend, is why the Almighty has not seen fit, at this point in time, to give them their extra teeth. Twenty-eight, that's all they've got, and if they persist in their pagan ways, that's all they'll ever fuckin' get!'

I was dumb-founded.

'There's your answer,' said Fisty, as he raised his warm glass and finished the dregs of a pint which had been lying in the bottom for over half an hour.

Standing up he thumped his hook on the table, and bade me good night. His lecture for that day was now at an end.

For a few years I really believed old Fisty's stories, taking his advice to the letter, and always checking them out first. But in the end I discovered it was just old stories old men dreamt up for young boys, and I had fallen for them - hook, line and sinker.

I soon found out that fannies hadn't a tooth in their heads, but little insects which lived in the immediate vicinity definitely had. These countless thousands of champing, gnashing, chewing little bastards were known in Northern Ireland at the time as 'The Crabs'. These days you never hear the name mentioned.

22

On one occasion, and on one occasion only, I went out with a girl who lived on the outskirts of Enniskillen, a town better known to local people as Skintown.

She had easily the best body I'd ever seen: round, yet firm, and inviting to the touch. It felt like velvet and it was easy to understand why it was in such constant demand.

She would strip off to her pelt in a field by the roadside, and allow you to ride her. Oblivious to passing traffic, pedestrians or cows looking over hedges, the act of sex saw her standing upright, and gazing towards the horizon in Red Indian fashion.

During the operation she would never utter one word, or make a sound, and if emotion was a part of Peggy's make up, then she definitely didn't give anything away.

It was rumoured, recalled and sworn upon in those years, that she would take on up to ten men in succession, and then throw in a teenage virgin at the end for good luck!

The story was told that one such youngster, long tired of waiting for the ten men to finish, kept running up and down the field, shouting uncontrollably, 'Where will I put it, where will I put it?' The older men had to lift him on, and then lift him off when it was all over.

A week or so after my own encounter with her, I was changing for bed in the light of a bare sixty watt bulb, which came out of the wall at ninety degrees, just above the headboard. (A light shade at that angle would have looked plain silly, so it remained as it was, unadorned but practical).

When pulling on my pyjamas I thought for a moment that I saw something moving and glistening on my pubic hair, as if it was being occupied by some strange swarm.

That shining, rippling silver, will forever remind me of the song made famous by The Clancy Brothers and Tommy Makem, 'The Shoals of Herring'.

23

'Oh my good, sweet, holy fuck. What the hell can it be?' I couldn't ask my father and mother because I knew they would kill me. I'd be strangled, if I was lucky!

On second thoughts, my eyes could have been playing tricks on me; after all, the light in the bedroom was far from good. I would look again, even though my fear was growing by the second.

Jamming the back of the chair under the door handle, I jumped onto the bed, and with my pubic hair only inches from the sixty watt, my worst fears were realised. There were twice as many of them as before. They were multiplying.

'Oh my sweet, holy fuck, I'm really fucked now. What am I going to do?' I panicked.

I immediately thought of her and wondered how she could do this to me. The fact that she 'courted' both Catholics and Protestants was my main consolation, for at the very least it proved it wasn't sectarian. What a relief!

These boyos were her property all right, and the funniest thing about this whole sad episode was I couldn't give them back.

Going down into the kitchen, which in those days was called a scullery, I filled the big tin basin with boiling water, fresh from the kettle, lifted the newest bar of carbolic soap I could find and grabbed one of those big hand scrubbing brushes shaped like a boat, which my mother used on the front door step every Monday morning.

Back in the bedroom behind a tightly closed door, I told myself that this would shift the bastards. I couldn't see any on my Willie, but they were having a field day a short distance to the North.

Big brush and soap were now making serious contact in the water, until the bristles became a steaming, bubbling mass of roasting lather. Then my work began: Scrub! Scrub!! Scrub!!!

'Christ, this is sore, but I must keep going.' The war was now definitely on, and no hope of a ceasefire.

24

Backwards and forwards, then up and down, and just in case I missed a few, round and round as well. I scrubbed in places where they hadn't even reached yet, just in case they got any smart ideas about moving on.

The Chinese proverb my father had told me, some months earlier, now came rushing back to mind; 'He that dippeth the wick shall pay for the paraffin'. Smart fuckers, those Chinese! After five minutes of fierce friction of brush on skin I felt sure they'd had enough.

Squatting directly over the basin, I splashed myself, to remove excess suds, before climbing back up onto the bed once again, for another inspection under the sixty watt.

Holy Christ and all the Saints, they're still there moving away, and I'm now as raw as a butcher's shop. I'd be eaten alive. I didn't sleep much that night, rising every hour or so for a body count.

Getting up at 8.30 am the first thing I did was check the 'battlefield'. I mightn't have bothered doing so, because they were still there in millions.

Push bike at the ready, and my excuse perfectly rehearsed, I set out for the Chemist's in Lisnaskea. Chemists were life-savers in those days, concerning anything to do with sexually transmitted diseases. Doctors were too formal, and weren't to be trusted, and anyway they had a terrible habit of writing everything down.

An old-timer once asked me the difference between 'sex' and 'riding'? 'To have sex,' he said, 'you need education, but any ould prick could get a ride.' I never forgot that and believed it made a lot of sense.

Condoms, or French Letters as we called them, were well known for putting up a good fight against Syphilis or Gonorrhoea, but the boys who were presently eating me alive, and on my bicycle, only laughed their heads off at such protection. They were smart little fuckers alright.

In a back room of the Chemist's in Lisnaskea, there I was, with my trousers around my ankles and with new shining underpants stretched nervously across spread, shaking knees. I was sixteen years of age.

25

The Chemist was a tall, thin man in a white coat and wearing gold rimmed glasses. Lowering himself on one knee and pulling the glasses down to the end of his long nose, for greater magnification, he looked closely at the infected area.

'And where did you pick up these boys, young Hanvey?', he asked, in one deep breath, as he put his right hand on his knee, and stood up straight again.

'Off a - off - I got them off a toilet seat,' I shuddered.

'Aye, that's where they come from alright,' he agreed.

I said to myself, 'He's one stupid fucker.'

'Have you got anything for them,' I asked.

'I think if you don't feed them soon, you'll be eaten alive,' he quipped.

'For God's sake hurry. What do they eat?' I asked.

'Bacon and eggs, but not many doctors know that,' he smiled.

'Oh my good fuck. Maybe he's telling the truth!'

Calmly pulling out small steps, he slowly climbed until his hand was able to reach the top shelf, which was full with bottles of all colours, and boxes of every shape and size.

Retrieving a small waxen box, from behind some bigger ones, he slowly descended.

'For fuck's sake would you hurry up!' I yelled.

This was the magic stuff alright. I'd heard about it before: 'Blue Ointment'.

'Rub this on every morning and night, and make sure you don't miss their heads. That's how they do the damage, with their heads,' he said in all seriousness.

'Oh my good, sweet Jesus, I'll have to kill myself.'

'So away you go, young Hanvey, and don't do it again,' he concluded.

'That's it definitely over for me. From now on there'll be no more strange toilets. I'll shite in the hedge first, if I have to,' I vowed. The Blue Ointment killed the crabs alright, and I was never bothered with them again.

It had been a close shave, in more ways than one.

'THE NEWS OF THE WORLD'

Every Sunday morning on the 'deeply disturbed' ward one anxious solitary patient paced up and down, staring at the big, main door with unbelievable anticipation, as the remaining twenty-nine inmates sat on green, plastic covered chairs, some of which had those white, uneven cubes of foam rubber sticking out of them from places which were always visible.

This was my favourite ward to work in.

The patients were mobile, had good personal hygiene, and from Monday to Friday they worked in Male Four gardens, cutting sticks, weeding, digging, generally doing the things everyone does in their own garden. In exchange for their work, which was also good therapy, they received tuck money to spend in the Hospital Shop.

Any moment now, that big, heavy door, strongly reinforced with Georgian wire glass would reverberate to the sound of Charlie's fist banging for admission. As regular as clockwork, he delivered the papers and his timing, they said, was more accurate than Big Ben's.

Old Jimmy was pacing faster now, twisting his wrist and closely looking at it, even though he didn't own a watch. His anxiety was at bursting point.

I didn't need to take his pulse because I knew it would be 'way on the wrong side of a hundred, and well above the 'normal' rate of seventy-two beats per minute.

'For God's sake, Charlie, would you be early for once, before Jimmy has a heart attack,' I wished.

The ward clock showed ten o'clock exactly, and as the second hand swept the twelve, the echo of the door being thumped shook every corner of the day room, boot store, dormitory and washroom.

Charlie had arrived, and Jimmy was already on the spot, gazing through the glass at him.

'Keys, Nurse! Keys, Nurse!! Keys, Nurse!!!' roared Jimmy, 'Door! Door! Door!'

As soon as I had turned the lock, Jimmy reached out, and grabbed the Sunday papers from Charlie. 'The Sunday News'; 'The Sunday Press'; 'The Sunday Independent' and the 'Sunday Times' were all thrown carelessly on the day room table, but Jimmy's favourite, The News of the World, was lovingly folded and placed under his left arm, as he slowly strolled to his chair, which occupied the middle space in a long row below the windows.

It took me over a month to discover what Jimmy was up to because Senior Nurses, at that time, believed Students' training would be more efficient if they learned to diagnose for themselves the peculiarities and mannerisms associated with the different types of mental illnesses.

Jimmy's nose was much bigger than mine; red and swollen, with countless little capillaries criss-crossing it at every opportunity, giving the impression he had been a whiskey drinker, which he wasn't.

'Nurse Hanvey, Jimmy's only a cunt; and you're a big silly cunt too, Nurse.'

'I know, John Joseph, I know.'

John Joseph hated the ward to be tranquil, and you could bet money on him 'raring up' as soon as all the patients were seated comfortably.

For over a month of Sundays I had passed Jimmy as he read the paper, and something in the back of my mind told me that things weren't quite as they seemed. I figured he just wasn't reading the paper correctly, so I decided to sit down and engage in a little discreet detective work.

Sitting opposite, I could see the big broad sheet covered the upper half of his body completely, and all that remained visible were two knees, two legs and two immaculately polished boots, with the front and back pages reflecting beautifully, on carefully buffed toecaps.

'Your bum's a plum, Nurse. Your bum's a fuckin' plum.' John Joseph was at it again. Things were just too peaceful for him.

'Nurse, shut him fuckin' up, the illiterate bastard,' said a voice from deep within The News of the World. John Joseph was interrupting Jimmy's reading and he did not like it one little bit.

This was the spark that lit the bonfire. Now a babble of voices all aimed at John Joseph gained volume and intensity.

'Shut the silly bastard up!'

'He's only silly!'

'The cunt's silly!'

'Stick the big needle in his arse, Nurse!'

'Kill him, Nurse!'

'Kill the whingeing fucker!'

All this aggression was too much for old Bertie The Butt who was taking it all in but decided there was too much talk and not enough action.

Standing upright on his chair, he took deadly aim at John Joseph who was still stirring up the crowd. Roaring at the top of his voice he assumed the pose for which he was famous - The Aeroplane!

For a man of sixty-five he moved like a tank, only faster, and I knew there was no way I could stop the rapidly unfolding series of events which was already in motion.

For a start, John Joseph had his back to The Butt, and was so involved in disturbing the ward it would take a miracle at the very least to engineer his escape. He was standing in the middle of the 'runway', and as the song says, 'The big 707 was set to go!'

Secondly, the goldfish tank sat at waist level on the dividing partition, which separated the day room from the door area, only two feet from John Joseph and directly in front of him.

The Butt thundered across the ward, head down, eyes closed and arms outstretched, but beautifully on course, and gaining speed by the second! I knew what was going to happen was inevitable, and I stood up. So did the rest of the patients.

They were cheering and shouting and baying for blood, but John Joseph never moved.

Whack!

The Butt's head buried itself deeply into the small of John Joseph's back, catapulting him right through the fish tank, which immediately disintegrated.

Water, rocks, algae, electric wire and fishes were here, there and everywhere. The ward was a shambles.

A dozen nurses in long, white coats from adjoining wards, quickly arrived as back-up, just in case the violence should spread, though, in stark contrast to similar scenes in the outside world, it never did.

The Butt, who had the strength of ten men, was gently overpowered, and held face down on the floor. An injection of Paraldehyde, a foul-smelling, almost instantaneous sedative, was quickly driven into his already bare right buttock, and as far as The Butt was concerned the war was over.

Paraldehyde is secreted from the body through the skin and the lungs giving an odour similar to cat's piss. Bertie wouldn't smell too pretty for a day or two!

Domestic staff flew into action with mops, brushes and small shovels, lifting every fragment of debris in sight.

Then I noticed something very peculiar - all the little goldfish, dozens of them, were no longer wriggling on the rubber surfaced floor. They had vanished.

Going over to a domestic, I asked, 'Where did the fish go? Did you see any fish?'

'No, I didn't, come to think of it. Did you see any fish, Doris?' she asked her mate.
'No, there's no fish here,' replied Doris.

As quickly as I could, I scanned the faces around the room.

I couldn't believe my eyes.

Big Davy was hunched in his chair in the corner, with the peak of his chequered cap pulled down over the tip of his nose, giving him at least some limited cover - and chewing for all he was worth ...

'Stand up, Davy,' I said.

The shining orange tail of a goldfish poked out between his lips as he kept on munching, his mouth full to the teeth.

'Davy, I think you're eating the goldfish,' I suggested.

'Go away and fuck yourself, I'm eating no fuckin' goldfish,' he mumbled.

His words found great difficulty in making their way past such a mess of wanton destruction.

'Empty your pockets please, Davy.'

Davy did as I ordered, and at once one, two ... six ... ten ... fourteen ... trembling tiddlers showered to the floor. I told him to go and change his coat.

John Joseph, meanwhile, was up and about again, without a scratch. In fact, he had not come in contact with the water at all. He was as dry as a bone. All the aggro had disappeared, and as quiet as a mouse he waltzed across the room.

And through all this commotion Jimmy continued reading the newspaper as though nothing had happened.

'I want the paper, Nurse! I want the paper!' cried John Joseph.

'So much for 'The Aeroplane',' I thought.

'Get me the fuckin' paper, or I'll wreck the ward.'
I knew he wouldn't.

'He's not getting it,' bellowed Jimmy. 'Sure he can't read. The wee cunt can hardly walk, let alone read. He's getting no fuckin' paper; it's mine.'
'It's not; it's not; it's the ward's,' shouted John Joseph.

The paper still sat motionless, like a silent sail on a glassy sea. It was then my main focus of attention.

Now when people read newspapers they make noise. They turn and rattle pages; they shake the sheets to fold them over. But not Jimmy; he was sitting like a model in a waxworks museum!

Suddenly, the most almighty roar lanced my eardrums, as John Joseph rocketed three feet into the air, and landed squarely on the broad of his back, with blood pumping from a gash in the back of his head.

His face was alive with twitches, and froth and spittle had combined and flowed, ever so slowly, from the corner of his mouth. His eyes rolled as if searching for direction and his body shook uncontrollably all over.

He had also wet himself.

I checked to see if he had bitten or swallowed his tongue, and made sure his airway was clear.

He was O.K.

All the patients had gathered round in a circle, as if witnessing the scene of a traffic accident.

'Move back and give him air,' ordered the Charge Nurse. Everyone took one pace backwards, widening the circle.

'He's dead,' said one.

'No, not yet,' diagnosed another.

'Get the Doctor. Get the Priest. Get the Undertaker,' they all shouted. Then out of all the bedlam a lone, steady voice of reason calmly stated, 'It's only a fit.' It was that voice from The News of the World again.

John Joseph was carried to bed in the dormitory, to sleep it off, and tomorrow he would be back to his old tricks again.

Once more everything in the ward was peaceful. It was so quiet you could hear a body drop!

The paper opposite, had now developed a steady tremble, as I crept from my chair to investigate.

'The Nurse's up!' shouted Peter.

We called him 'The Early Warning System', because he had saved more lives in the hospital than any other. When fires broke out, or when pipes burst, or if patients were in difficulty he was the first to let the staff know. He had been traumatised during World War Two, but his upper crust English accent was a source of tranquillity, and added a little class to the ward. If the hospital was being demolished by a series of explosions Peter would more than likely calmly approach you and say, 'Excuse me, Nurse, there's a series of explosions happening.'

He was as cool as death.

Jimmy never budged.

I quickly sat down again, just in case Jimmy spotted me.

'Nurse's down again,' reported Peter, loudly.

'I'll sicken you, Peter,' I said to myself, as I began standing up and sitting down in rapid succession.

'Nurse's up; Nurse's down; Nurse's up; Nurse's down,' repeated Peter, as I finally collapsed back into my chair.

'Nurse is now seated sensibly,' said The Daily Mail man.

Peter never missed a trick, and if he never missed a trick I believed he would surely know what Jimmy was up to behind the paper. After all, he had been watching him for years.
I walked over towards him.

'Nurse is approaching from North/North-West.'

'Nurse has now arrived, and is sitting down.'
'Good, morning Nurse, and how are we today? I've just been enjoying forty winks,' he said in his rich 'Officer's' accent.

'Peter, could you tell me one thing,' I whispered.

'Most certainly Nurse; let me have it.'

'What is Jimmy doing behind that newspaper?'

'It's very simple, old boy. You don't have to be a Constable to figure that one out.'

By now I was twenty feet from Jimmy, this time seeing him in three quarters profile.

'Watch his left hand,' said Peter. 'Because that chap Jimmy is left-handed. Do you follow so far, Nurse?'

'Yes, I do,' I answered.

'Do you see his pocket move Nurse? Now tell me what you see.'

'He's interfering with himself, that's what he's doing.'

'Masturbating, old chap. Always stick rigidly to the English language, and don't be afraid to call a spade a spade. Now, go over and see what page he's at and watch out for his nose.'

'His nose?' I questioned.

'Yes, his nose; don't forget his nose,' said Peter.

Tiptoeing up beside Jimmy I noticed the pocket was still moving and sure enough the page revealed a big photograph of an unusually healthy looking girl, with big breasts, sitting on a bale of hay.

Without a doubt, this picture was aimed fairly and squarely at the male members of the farming community because right behind her, and slightly to the left, sat a big Ferguson tractor. A few pitchforks and shovels lay against a sheet of corrugated iron, helping to complete the illusion of a peaceful rustic scene.

'You're masturbating, Jimmy,' I ventured.

'I'm not fuckin' wankin',' he responded angrily, as The News of the World started shaking like a Poltergeist.

'What happened to your nose, Jimmy?' I asked.

'There's nothing wrong with my fuckin' nose,' he snapped. 'Go away to the mirror and look at your own nose, and give my head peace.'

The tip of his nose was as black and shiny as his boots. The editor and photographers of that most popular of 'Sundays' never failed to deliver the goods, and supplied the bould Jimmy with a new girl every week; she was never late, and always arrived at ten on the dot.

Wetting my finger on my tongue, I touched his nose to see if the black stuff would come off, and sure enough it did, as Jimmy jerked his head to the side in disgust.

'It's black newsprint,' confirmed Peter.

He was right yet again. Jimmy had been kissing the photograph.

'Nurse is turning now; Nurse is walking across the floor; this time, South, South West. Nurse is sitting down.'

'Well! What a morning that one's been.'

There was never a dull moment in the deeply disturbed ward.

'SING ME SOME BOB DYLAN'

Her perfectly laundered, blue uniform bulged heavily underneath the name tag, telling me in no uncertain terms she was a Ward Sister.

It was a strong position to hold in the world of nursing at the time, and one which was guaranteed to drive fear into the hearts of young Student Nurses like me.

In my nursing career to date I had gone out with an Occupational Therapy Student from County Galway, an International Voluntary Student from London and a State Enrolled Nurse who never moved or uttered a sound during The Grand National. It was over Beecher's Brook, into the Canal Turn and up the homeward straight in complete silence.

She never made a big deal out of 'the act' itself and I must say I admired her honesty. With her, the 'Ohs' and 'Ahs' which were popular with most other girls I'd met, simply didn't exist.

Her lungwork was kept to a minimum and her whole demeanour revolved around the passion of conserving energy. Although her eighteen stones relegated her to the class of comfort and not speed, she was nevertheless a super girl who, I suspect, only had sex simply so as not to be left out of the flow of social activity which existed in Downshire at the time.

I, too, often wondered what it was all about, and quietly questioned the gurgling, moaning, cursing, screeching, and screaming, which nearly always accompanied the female climax.

My mate Billy, from Belfast, who had easily the sharpest Northern wit I ever encountered, summed them up like this; 'They're comedians! They'd give you a fuckin' pain in the head listening to them!'

Fisty on the other hand, had his own personal theory, which he imparted to me during one of his countless lectures.

He said women would roar and shout, wriggle and giggle, and do almost anything to get it over with quickly. He insisted the thing which they liked most about sex was the cigarette afterwards!

'That was the only time when their species ever showed any human tendencies,' he would conclude.

Over the years, on such occasions I would also roll over onto my back, and enjoy a 'puff', always thinking to myself, 'That man Fisty was a genius.'

He always maintained there were four types of female orgasm; one, the Religious; Oh God! Oh God!! Oh God!!!

Two, the Positive; Oh Yes! Oh Yes!! Oh Yes!!!

Three, the Negative; Oh No! Oh No!! Oh No!!!

Four, the Faked; Oh Bobbie! Oh Bobbie!! Oh Bobbie!!!

Fisty told me he had spent five years at Queen's University 'doing exams to be a gynaecologist', but was sacked on his very first day of ward duty after the Senior Consultant told him his hands were too big!

The Occupational Therapy Student from Galway was a good girl who only just tolerated my 'hand jobs', always turning her back on me for the duration, and then always blessing herself when it was over!

This was her way of letting me know that she wasn't as yet ready for this kind of business, but despite my faults she liked me just the same.

Our favourite meeting place was always the potting shed in Male Four garden where we'd sit on bags of fertiliser and sing songs together, to the sound of my old twelve string guitar.

Fellow nurses who had seen me leaving the 'Home' with my instrument would remark when they saw me next morning, 'You were out singing again last night.'

'Aye it was a great concert, but only one person showed up.'

Bob Dylan was number one then, and every evening, after I'd done the 'unspeakable', and she had turned her back and blessed herself, she would whisper softly 'Bobbie, please sing me some Bob Dylan,' and I always did. I figured she looked upon this as my penance and I thought it was a fair enough exchange!

She was big-boned and ruggedly beautiful like the county she came from. High, gaunt cheekbones and fair, freckled skin, which had been nurtured on strong winds from the Atlantic, still showed the child in the face of this lovely young woman.

Dylan's 'The Times They Are A Changin'' was her favourite song. Any time my father heard it on the radio he would shake his head at the set, and comment, 'Aye, and they're not changin' much for the better.' Now, thirty years later, it was my turn to repeat his words. Life sure was one short, old game. Fisty used to say, 'Everyone is rushing to nowhere, and knocking everybody else down trying to get there.'

My old friend Joe Stratton compared the way life has changed to the ticking of two clocks. The old 'wag of the wall' came from an age of caring and relaxation, and everything about it, from the way it was made, to the way it looked, oozed class at every chime. Its tick was slow, deliberate and almost hypnotic as it told us to, 'Tick your time; tick your time; tick your time.'

On the other hand the modern electric clock looked like plastic, as if it was made in a hurry, which it was.

It had neither class or respect, but its tick which was repeated furiously told us to, 'Get up and get at it; get up and get at it; get up and get at it.'

I love Joe's story of the two clocks.

The last I heard of my old friend from Galway was that she emigrated to Australia, and was nursing out there.

Sometimes I wondered if she'd return to Ireland at the end of her days, and be buried in the same ground as all of her friends from the sixties. It would be nice if it could end like that, and then we'd all be together again.

40

The International Voluntary Student from London was also a 'child of the sixties' who loved folk music and sitting round bonfires on long, summer evenings, talking about all the wrongs in the world, and how we might put them right.

Like all English girls she had good manners and was just as shrewd as, if not more shrewd than, the Irish themselves, with the added veneer of innocence thrown in for confusion. Just like at home! With hair so fair it was almost white, her sea blue eyes were the bluest I'd ever seen in the head of a human being. They could change colour with her moods, but always different shades of blue. When I gazed into them, I could both see and hear the ocean, only there was no way she was letting me into her 'life boat'! As far as I was concerned, she was the Titanic and no one was about to put her down.

She would say her religion allowed her to sleep with Catholics like me, but forbade intercourse.

'Some fuckin' religion that,' I thought. 'They must be trying to drive Catholics astray in the fuckin' head!' Her religion had originally been Protestant, but she'd given it up to join this other crew, who had been gaining momentum in the sixties.

The International Voluntary Students came to Downshire every summer from England, Scotland and Wales; from Germany and France and God only knows where else. They would dig gardens, pull weeds and generally tidy up the hospital grounds. In exchange for their work the Hospital Authority would give them rooms in the Nurses' Homes and food in the canteen, but as far as getting money was concerned, they didn't.

Unlike the Orangemen, who lit their bonfires on the eleventh night of July, these students would light one every night and sit round it, singing protest songs and drinking Coca Cola. They definitely knew how to enjoy themselves, and so did I.

Anyway, my friend's name was Rebecca and we'd talk about the thing all young people talk about - getting married!

I used to like talking about it, and soon discovered that a good line to put them in the right frame of thought was, 'How many babies would you like?' If she said 'Six' then you knew, at the very least, she would let you ride her six times.

Fisty would have said, 'If you're wise, you'll keep talking about it!'

'Rebecca.'

'Yes, Bobbie.'

'Tell me this.'

'If I can,' she smiled.

'Right! You tell me your religion allows you to sleep with me, but it doesn't allow sex with Catholics.'

'Correct.'

'Now unless I'm mistaken, did we not, just a few minutes ago, indicate that we could get married?'

'We did.'

'Some marriage that would turn out to be with no 'Dan',' I joked.

'What's Dan?'

'Now Rebecca, don't tell me you come from England and don't know what Dan is. Sure doesn't your country run on Dan? 'Dan der an Dan,' I sang. 'Just like the music on television from the American detective series.'

'We're not allowed to watch television. What's Dan? Please tell me.' 'I'll do better than that, I'll show you. Why do you not watch television?' I diverted.

'It's against our religion.'

'That's fair enough,' I answered.

I was now undoing the buttons on my trousers and at the same time trying hard to imagine what life must be like without television. I bet her mother put a small table, complete with a vase of flowers, where the television was supposed to be, or perhaps she pulled the bookcase out from the wall a foot or two at an angle to create an illusion, and hoped their neighbours would not notice.

Sitting eagle-eyed, and spread eagled on my bed beside me, she quietly asked, 'What are you doing?'

'I'm getting Dan out,' I replied, as I fought with the last, tight button. 'Now Rebecca, this is Dan. Would you like to shake hands with him?'

'Alright, I'm allowed to do that,' she gently smiled, still trying to maintain her facade of rapidly declining innocence.

'This is the first time I've seen Dan,' she said, as she proceeded to hold him in both hands.

'Who the fuck does she think she's trying to kid? Go away and give my head peace,' I thought.

'Well, would you look at that,' I wondered. Her head got lower and, Holy Moses, she had Dan in her mouth. I hoped she wasn't an epileptic! The last thing I needed was more Russian Roulette!

No sex with Catholics, eh? She must have been upside down, and didn't know her arse from her elbow. Still, it did just fine as Dan seemed to be enjoying himself.

With Rebecca, life revolved above the waist. She would allow me to see 'it'; touch it; rub Dan against it, but as far as 'asking me in' was concerned, it simply wouldn't happen. She sort of stuck to her religion alright!
I saw her a few years after that and she hadn't changed. She would ring me up from England and ask how was Dan, and I'd give her as accurate a report as I could, depending on how things were at the time.

I would say, 'Oh, he's sleeping right now,' or 'He's just getting up,' or 'Don't talk to me, he's just after being sick all over the place.'

Then suddenly, I never heard from her again. Perhaps she'd found a bigger and better Dan, and had bought a twenty-two inch television.

'THE RAILWAY STATION'

Enniskillen's old railway station was wrecked, run down and dilapidated. It was in a sorry state of affairs, although I didn't realise it at the time.

Two years earlier, in 1957, someone decided the trains had no need to run there any more and since then, they'd remained silent, enjoying a well-earned rest.

Although derelict with floors in upstairs rooms full of vandalised holes and dangerous to walk on, the buildings had retained their character and provided Mickey The Dog Flannigan and me with the best hiding places available, when we mitched school, which was often.

At fourteen, I was attending Enniskillen Tech. In a previous life this depressing, gloomy place, peppered randomly with black Nissen huts, had been a prison and still had the high imposing wall to prove it. I just couldn't wait for the day when my release would be announced. In those bleak, grey days of the nineteen fifties when Christmas cards looked as they were supposed to look, sex education hadn't been invented and therefore wasn't included in the curriculum.

On the other hand, the College sick room was a constant source of exploration and learning. It occupied little space at the end of the main hall, over to the right and just below the stairs. In such a hotbed of authoritarian morality I was never able to understand how boys and girls could arrange to be 'unwell' at the same time and end up spending all day under the blankets together.

The only stipulation was, if two pupils of the opposite sex were in there at the same time, the Yale lock must not be snibbed. I was sick so often I enjoyed it and dreaded the day when good health would revisit my life again. Sometimes, I even prayed for a relapse.

In the late nineteen fifties the word sex was not a common one in the County Fermanagh. When a new word was imposed upon the local population, people tended to avoid it like the plague and reverted to using older ones their fathers and grandfathers had used. This was one way of trying to stem progress.

Words which hadn't been used in an age were carefully plucked from ancient drawers and released into circulation once again. Alternatives used to describe the brilliance of sexual gymnastics were shaggin', ridin', buffin', jumpin' and leppin'. These, it appeared, were preferable and fitted in more comfortably with the highs and lows of the local accent.

While riding was looked upon as an achievement beyond our wildest dreams, the main topic of conversation which seemed to constantly preoccupy the boys was the age-old question always asked the morning after, 'Did you get your hand on it?'

To us, getting our hand on it was the ultimate victory, with the ride always seeming to be something for the future, which would happen when the time was right.

My best friend at the Tech. was Mickey The Dog Flannigan and we constantly played truant, spending our days smoking in the countless rooms of that old railway station.

Our favourite eating house, 'The Golden Arrow' was known as having the best fish and chips in the country.

Elvis was on the juke-box, in fact he was seldom off it, when she sauntered in with her bulging schoolbag hanging carelessly from one shoulder.

As I was in the process of devouring a fish supper she slithered into the seat beside me.

'You're Bobbie Hanvey, aren't you?'

'Yes, I am.'

'I'm Concepta O'Halloran.'

'Hello Concepta.' I could see from the colour and cut of her school uniform she attended the local convent.

'Hi Bobbie. Excuse me for sitting down like this, but you may be able to help me.'

'If I can,' I replied, realising that anyone who was looking for my help must be in dire difficulties and close to ending it all.

'You and The Dog spend a lot of time up at the old railway station,' she suggested.

It was in those musty old cubicles of former gleam and steam that The Dog and I cut our eye teeth on some matters which related to the opposite sex.

'And how do you know we be up there,' I asked nervously.

'Everybody knows that. It's all over the town that you and The Dog almost live up there.'

'And what if we do,' I answered abruptly thinking she might be spying for the Mother Superior, who in turn would 'sell us out' to our Principal, Mr Hanna. I mightn't have worried.

Resting her face on her hands in the way most girls did in chip-shops, during the late fifties, I almost choked, as her bluntness hit me like a hammer.

'Bobbie, I don't know much about it, but I would be grateful, if you would take me up the station and show me your Willie,' which was exactly what she called it.

In those years, girls on the edge of womanhood would go out with boys, not to get a ride, but simply to see what a Willie looked like. When they made the simple transition from ankle to knee length socks all the boys knew the cat was well and truly out of the bag and the time had come for action.

Concepta wore knee length socks and I took this, rightly or wrongly, as some sort of a signal.

I agreed to mitch school the next day and to meet her in the room above the Station Master's office at 11.00 am.

I hated maths so much I refused to wear a wrist watch for years. Algebra and all that stuff was double dutch and I could never understand it, so missing a class such as that was not only a God-send, it was a necessity.

My maths teacher lived almost beside me in Brookeborough and each day, before his class, in all the years attending that jail, Mr Taylor stuck the money in my fist, gave me a leg up over the high perimeter wall and told me to bring him back a pound of Roses. Popular sweets at the time, some local people believed they could grow on you.

He simply loved and was addicted to Roses.

Every morning at 6.00 am in hail, rain, or snow, the slap, slap, slap, slap of loose gutties scuffed, squelched and pounded their way past the corner of our house at 5 Main Street.

Jogging had yet to be invented in Northern Ireland but Mr Taylor was already at it. Locals maintained he was definitely the first to do it.

No one in the village ever made a point of rising early. Even the cock seldom crowed before seven, which meant few people actually saw him heading out the Lisnaskea Road in his Daz white vest and matching broad, baggy trunks.

Around the twelfth of July when suspicions of the 'other side' became slightly magnified, various individuals from within both traditions would help to heighten tensions by releasing certain rumours which being harmless enough in themselves, provided hungry minds with much needed food for thought.

Paddy McCluskey sat where he always sat, at the left hand side of the long, shiny counter in Jim O'Donnell's pub. Always wearing his cap as he faced his pint, Paddy was the best carpenter in Ireland. Being a superb story-teller, local lads who had called in for their evening drink enjoyed 'winding him up', or so they thought.

'Did you hear about the sums master who lives down the Tanyard Lane?'

'I did,' nodded Paddy as he took the first gulp from his pint.

'He's supposed to be running out the road every morning before anybody's up,' volunteered Andy.

'He is,' replied Paddy, quietly studying how these young bucks could be taught a lesson.

'They say he does all this running in his vest and underpants wearin' an oul' done pair of gutties.'

'Do they now. Aye, I suppose they do,' replied Paddy showing the bare minimum of interest.

'We hear you're still teaching your canaries how to whistle Paddy!'

'I am,' he smiled, knowing this line of talk was only a diversion and sooner or later they'd once again return to the sums master.

'I suppose they're good at the whistlin' now,' rasped McNulty.

Slowing and methodically filling his pipe, Paddy looked at them with quiet contempt and quickly looked away again.

'You 'shuda' heard the racket in our house at five o'clock the smornin'. The wife nearly took the hinges off the bedroom door and the 'tares' of her down the stairs, and she was out on the Main Street, before she realised it wasn't the local flute band practisin' for the twelfth. Oh, my canaries can whistle alright.'

The bar was in an uproar as Paddy gave a fleeting smile and once again returned to his pint.

He had won round one.

'You were tellin' us the sums master was out runnin',' stabbed Murphy.

'I was indeed,' he agreed.

'Do you think there's any truth in it?'

'Oh there's truth in it alright,' sparked Paddy as he pulled peacefully on his pipe and continued to gaze on his own reflection in the bar mirror.

'You'll not know this, but I'm the only man in the town that's seen him.'

'You're jokin',' they returned, wondering whether to believe him or not. Paddy had the name of being an early riser so they figured anything was possible.

'At five the smornin' I was takin' the dog out for a walk when your man ...'

'The sums master,' they interrupted.

'The very man and him runnin' like a Protestant from Midnight Mass, with his big togs brattlin' in the wind like a line of washin', and him wearin' the biggest Orange Sash you've ever seen, with snakes and ladders and badges of King William scattered all over it.'

The entire gathering was mesmerised by the pictures he was painting and eagerly hanging on to his every word.

'Jazus,' exclaimed one.

'You're fuckin' jokin',' queried another.

'So you think so,' retaliated Paddy.

'Maybe he's right,' wavered Murphy.

'Well, God's my judge and I swear by all the Saints and all that's holy that I seen him alright.'

Paddy had now pulled in very reliable witnesses and no Catholic worth his salt would dare to question such a line-up, and any Protestants present, as usual, didn't get involved.

The boozers were now busy arguing amongst themselves and the bould Paddy had gained the high moral ground.

'I suppose youse all never thought to yourselves why he does all this runnin'. Did youse ever wonder where he goes, because you know as well as I do that he doesn't do it for the good of his health.'
'Where does he go?' they asked.

'Well I asked myself the same question and that's one of the reasons why I follied him the smornin'.'

'You followed him!' exclaimed Joe in amazement, not for a moment realising that Paddy was in his seventies and slowing up.

'I did, and I'll tell you where he finished up. In the Parochial House with Father Cullinan.'

'You've got to be fuckin' jokin',' stammered Murphy.

'Only I had the foresight to peep through the window I might never have found out what they were up to,' he winked.

'Aw, for fuck's sake would you hurry up and get it over with,' rushed Murphy who had now well and truly risen to the bait.

'Easy on. Take your time,' steadied Paddy. 'There I was peepin' through the window and there they were, sittin' in the parlour. Father Cullinan hadn't shaved for a week and was sittin' in an open-necked shirt and your man Taylor was sitting' upright opposite him with the sash wrapped round his neck like a life-belt.'

'But what were they doin'?' insisted Murphy.

'What were they doin'? What were they doin'?? I'll tell you what they were doin'. Playin' poker, that's what they were doin', and enough money sittin' on the table between them to choke an ass!'

'They were like hell,' dismissed Murphy.

'Well, there you have it,' swallowed Paddy as he lowered the remainder of his pint. He knew all aspects of life could be judged by the law of thirds and this unwritten law had now taken over. One third of the boys would believe him. One third wouldn't and the final third wouldn't care one way or the other.

Enough voices would carry the story further afield and sow a little mystery and mystique in the village.

My father knew Jonathan Taylor well and with this in mind I had decided not to return to his class when he would send me over the wall in the morning.

The Dog, who had already known of my plans, was yelping in anticipation and agreed the Roses would be as good in our bellies as anyone elses.

At 10.30 am Mickey was hiding in the damaged roofspace already in position, to watch the promised performance.

I paced up and down through broken timber and rubble, constantly on the look-out to see if she had arrived. I was as nervous as a young priest waiting to hear his first confession.

Every now and again the voice from above would peal out, 'Any sign of her yet?'

'No, not yet. For God's sake shut up or she'll hear you. You'll scare her off.'

Suddenly, a voice from the floor below shouted, 'Bobbie, are you up there?' It was her.

'Yes Concepta, I'm up here. Come on up,' I answered.

I quickly realised I had now two major worries. What I was about to do was a worry, and my second, and almost as big a worry was The Dog.

'Mickey, she's here,' I whispered loudly.

'I can hear that. Bet you can't get the knickers off her,' he scoffed.

'Would you shut up for God's sake? If I do manage to get them to her knees, will you give me a fag?' I panicked.

'Fair enough,' he replied as he began keeping as quiet as a mouse but giving the odd tee hee to help keep me on edge.

Concepta picked her way into the room brushing the dust from her school uniform blazer. The walls were flaking and she was covered in it. The Dog was silent.

'Jesus, I hope Flannigan doesn't start laughing and wreck the whole meeting,' I thought, as I gave a quick glance upwards to check, hoping she wouldn't notice.

'Hi Bobbie,' she said shyly.

'Hello Concepta,' I smiled, just as shyly, only trying hard not to show it.

'Go on show it to me,' she stumbled.

'Show you what,' I teased.

'Your Willie,' she pointed.

'Before I show you mine Concepta I think it's only fair that you show me yours.'

'O.K. Bobbie, but you mustn't put anything near it,' she pleaded, once again pointing at the fork of my trousers. 'Now promise me you'll not do that,' she repeated.

'Fair enough, but can I touch it with my hands,' I bargained.

'Well, I suppose so, I'm sure that wouldn't do much harm,' she said.

'Jesus,' I wondered, 'What were the nuns in the convent filling her head with.'

Before I had time to do any more wondering she had her back to the wall to the left of the broken window panes and was pulling down an enormous pair of white bloomers.

I was now looking at the blackest, hairiest face I'd ever seen and in all honesty I'd only seen two.

As I reached out to touch it with my left hand, although I was right handed, her knickers flashed upwards in front of me with the speed of a faulty window-blind. Swoosh - and that was it, gone. It was gone. Fisty had already warned me at one of his many lectures that black, hairy faces were the most deceptive things on earth. 'They were like watches and clocks.' He would then elaborate, 'Basically they all did the same job, but their faces were different.'

'Fisty's a fuckin' genius,' I thought.

'Right,' she rushed. 'You've seen mine, now let me see yours.'

In a situation like this, when my hand was being forced, Fisty told me to utter the words, 'Not so fast.' This he said, would have the desired effect of stunning her momentarily and giving me more time to think.

'Not so fast,' I argued. 'The deal was, I would definitely show you mine, but you would show me yours first and I could touch it and look at it closely, but you were too quick.'

'I said you could touch it, but I never said you could look at it,' she emphasised.

'Fuck this, the deal's off,' I stressed, as I pulled up my already open zip.

'But Bobbie, I'm desperate nervous,' she sighed, in a genuine troubled tone.

Little did she know that I was twice as nervous, but Fisty had taught me well and told me at times like this to be 'British' and wear a stiff upper lip.

Whatever the nuns had taught her wasn't doing either of us any good. I figured she believed she could get pregnant by the dust in the air.

In those days if a Willie wasn't standing you took it out, and if it was standing you pulled it out.

Anyway, I took it out and she immediately asked me if I could make it stand.

'Can I make it stand,' I laughed. 'Easy,' I boasted, because at fifteen all you had to do was say stand and it did. One word did the trick. Just like an obedient police dog; sit, stand, jump, lie down, heel. It was as easy as that. Nowadays it would take a book at bedtime or a good technician, but they're usually booked solid and hard to find.

She felt it, rubbed it, tried to bend it and finally pulled it, just to see how it worked.

'Can it fire?' she enquired.

'Can it fire?' I laughed. 'Of course it can fire, but not just yet!'

The Dog was still in the roofspace and as quiet as a mouse. I had no worries as far as he was concerned because we had had countless wanking competitions in this very same room. Whoever 'came' first collected two cigarettes. That was the name of the game.

Like the soap ad from the time, we would soon have pulsating boiling action with the results being whiter than white.

'Will it fire soon?' she asked as she constantly gazed at it and kept on pulling.

'Will it fire soon?' I giggled. 'Of course it'll fire soon. Just give it time. Don't worry Concepta, it won't be long now!'

Out of the blue, a dull, steady, thump, thump, thump, thump broke the deadly silence as it reached us from above. It was The Dog and it wasn't hard to figure out what he was at. He was wanking.

'What the hell's that?' she panicked, stopping her rhythm and gazing upwards at a damaged but now moving ceiling.

'It's, it's, it's the, it's the old waterpipes. They're knocking up here all the time; for God's sake keep going,' I diverted, as I placed her hand in position once again.

'Well fuck me, The Dog's one lousy horny bastard,' I thought. The fuckin' culchie and he promised he'd keep quiet.

Chug, chug, chug she went and proceeded to ignore the noise which was getting heavier and faster in the attic.

'Will it soon be ready?' she grinned, glancing at me for a second before returning her eyes to Willie.

'Will it soon be ready?' I mused. She must think it's a Christmas cake in the oven. 'Yes Concepta, it'll soon be ready, don't worry!'

'Get it to hurry up,' she urged.

'Look at it now, can you see it,' I prompted.

'I can indeed, I can indeed,' she enthused, keeping the pressure to a maximum. 'Isn't it grand,' she laboured, in a soft Galway brogue despite having been born and bred in Enniskillen.

It was now spitting at her and 'painting' the walls of the office and I was roaring and shouting very much louder than was necessary, just to give her some encouragement for doing such a great job.

'Could you get it to do that again? Could you make it stand again?' she pleaded.

'It takes a wee while Concepta. Give it time. Give him a rest for a few minutes and then we'll see what happens, but first, you have to keep your half of the bargain and show me yours.'

'Only if you kneel down and don't stand up,' she insisted.

Five minutes later when I was down staring it straight in the face an unmerciful 'Aaah' reverberated from the roofspace. The Dog had hit the jackpot.

She looked up in horror, then at me, and then up again as he crashed through the thin ceiling and landed beside us in a cloud of white dust, plaster and rubble.
Bouncing to his feet he turned his back on her, pulled up his underpants and trousers at the same time and without waiting to fasten his belt, ran from the room holding them up in both hands.

Standing in shock with her knickers at her knees she slowly bent over and pulled them up. Brushing the dust from her jacket once again, she gave me a dirty look, pushed twenty Players Gold Leaf into my hand and never speaking as much as one word, departed.

Ten minutes later when I was sitting, dust to the neck, enjoying my cigarette, The Dog walked in grinning his head off from ear to ear and sat down beside me as if nothing had happened.

'Hanvey, give me a fag.'

'Here you culchie, light your own, but don't forget you owe me three. I came first!

'JANUARY 1967'

The patients were all tucked up and counted; all fifty of them.

The last round was done.

Dirty sheets in the psycho-geriatric ward were quickly disposed of; old men had been washed and made as comfortable as possible, and the yellow glow from the ward's night light transformed Bedlam into a new world, totally at ease with itself.

The constant hum from the air conditioning combined beautifully with the wall to wall ripple of snoring contentment. Sporadic, bouts of bad language guaranteed the more persistent hecklers at least another small measure of 'Largactil', before the sweet cloud of peace finally descended for the night.

Every evening, the pattern was the same.

Half nine ended my late shift, and after pulling off a brilliant white, knee-length coat (white that is, except for the scattered brown marks of 'collision' here and there) I would quickly wash my hands and face in the cloakroom and call it a day.

I had no way of knowing my life would begin in January 1967 and headed back through the ward for the solitude of the nurses' home.

The air-conditioning pressed louder on my eardrums as I saw a tall, slim figure dressed in the smart, blue uniform of a Student Nurse, step quietly out of the darkness, some six beds away.

The locker mirror to her right cast a perfect profile with neatly groomed fair hair, and white starched paper hat. I remember thinking with disbelief how anyone could appear so beautiful, and yet quite plain at the same time. Her very being radiated a joy with life which I had never encountered before.

Seeing her image in that low, half light reminded me of a picture my mother treasured in our County Fermanagh home; the simple, yet lingering beauty of the Blessed Virgin Mary, always dressed in blue and held in the highest regard possible, above all the Saints, His Holiness the Pope and even John F. Kennedy.

In those days, whenever a girl looked at me I saw myself through her eyes. Confidence was easy then.

In that haunting half darkness, her eyes cut into mine with that beautiful, despairing hopelessness of coming death, but the barely visible tremble of lips revealed a young girl shaking with innocent caution on the verge of womanhood.

A white, confident hand slid quietly from behind her apron top.

'Jesus, she sure has some spirit,' I thought, as she stood on the rubber-coated floor as if part of it.

Fine, perfect fingers reached out in my direction, as highly polished regulation black shoes remained firmly on the spot. I walked to within arm's length and our hands locked. I was now as nervous as she was.

Our eyes liked each other.

They never blinked or faltered as they absorbed what they saw, they ate each other with a great hunger.

They were busy doing what only eyes can do best, but now and again, in that short but never ending pause, they rested for a moment, to soon become busy again. They were at their work and we knew it.

A great silence surrounded me as the drone from the air conditioning retreated and was gone.

Nervous messages floated to and fro as our hands, now sweating and still, entwined in time in a constant ward temperature of eighty degrees.

'So you're the great Bobbie Hanvey,' she said. 'I'm Maggie Maguire, Student Nurse, and I'm pleased to meet you.'

'And I'm pleased to meet you too, Maggie Maguire.'

That was all it took.

'EASTER'

After Mass in the 'Great Hall' which was used for games and recreation for the patients, and also for dances, concerts and a cinema, we strolled the short distance to the Sugar Bowl where patients and staff would socialise and drink tea.

'Father Murphy gave a beautiful sermon,' she enthused, as she tossed the usual two spoonfuls of sugar into my cup.

'He did indeed, but it was a pity Wee Tessie jumped up when she did. I think he was very embarrassed.'

'Sure, isn't she always doing things like that? I'm sure he paid no attention and hardly even noticed,' she said dismissively.

I doubted very much if Father Murphy hardly noticed, as the disruption came at the most important part of the Mass. Father Pat was just about to raise the Host, as everyone was kneeling down with their heads bowed and breath bated when Wee Tessie escaped from her seat and took a long mad run the full thirty yards up the aisle, grinding to a halt six steps short of the altar.

One hundred heads turned like clockwork.

'Shoot her, Nurse!' cried a voice buried deep within the congregation.

'Hanging's too good for her!' piped another.

'Pagan!' shouted a third.

Soon, dozens of highly-charged, vitriolic comments were hurled in Tessie's direction, as she bounced into the air and landed flat on her face on the highly polished pine floor.

With her arms and legs flailing up and down in an awkward, sprawling movement she screamed, kicked and finally squealed, 'Father, would you exorcise me, Father? Exorcise me. The devil's in me. He's in me, Father! Do something quick; Ahhhhh ...'

Caustic comments from the shocked gathering stopped abruptly.

Either Father Pat hadn't been trained in the finer points of an exorcism or the Hierarchy believed there was a proper time and place for everything, but whatever the reason he slowly and respectfully raised the Host to a congregation suddenly oblivious as to their real reason for being there.

Tessie's screams simply intensified, drowning out the sharp, flurried rings of the Consecration bell.

Before the staff had time to muster and deliver the necessary restraint, Big Davy, who had stubbornly remained in the kneeling position waiting for the bell, jumped to his feet and with fat, massive fists uppercutting the air, he thundered, 'Hit her a big kick in the arse, Father! She's only a ... imm! imm! imm!'

Before Big Davy could complete this, the biggest line of his life, with the customary and automatic four letter word, a male nurse miraculously managed to muffle his mouth, with a well aimed right hand editing the sentence perfectly.

Both Tessie and Davy were unceremoniously removed, and taken back to their respective wards, and Mass continued and ended without further interruption.

'Would you like to go for a walk, Maggie?' I said, smiling again at the thought of Mass.

'I'd like that,' she agreed, as we pushed our chairs underneath the table and once again tasted the half-chill of a beautiful Easter morning.

Outside the Sugar Bowl old Harry was collecting freshly chucked butts from the ground and on spying us from the corner of his eye he immediately rushed over.

'Give us a butt Nurse; come on give us a butt. Have you got a fag Nurse? Go on give us a cigarette. I know you've got them Nurse. Give us one and I'll go away. Don't be so greedy Nurse. I know you've got plenty for I see the packet in your pocket, Nurse. Give us a fag. Go on give us a fag.'

'I don't smoke, Harry,' I replied.

'I know you smoke; I saw you and the Nurse smoking in the Sugar Bowl; you can't fool me,' he smiled, as he constantly rubbed his hands together in anticipation.

'Bobbie, would you please stop that and give him a cigarette,' she urged.

'Oh alright then, here's a fag, Harry.'

'Thanks, Nurse. Would you give me two? I have none for later.'

'O.K., here's two.'

'Go on Nurse; give me three and I'll have one for tomorrow.'

'That's all you're getting, Harry. Now away you go,' I said.

'Thanks Nurse; thanks Nurse.'

Turning to walk away I heard him mumble under his breath, 'Nurse is only a fucker - a rotten fucker. He's rotten. He can stick his fags up his arse.'

As I looked at Maggie she burst out laughing at the idea of old Harry conning two fags as nicely as you've ever seen.

'Do you believe I love you Maguire?'

'I do believe that.'

'Do you think it's possible I'll always love you?'

'I can think that as well,' she smiled.

Walking through the tall trees which looked magnificent by day, but most sinister during the hours of darkness, I noticed small pieces of twigs wafting earthwards, as careless crows who were too busy for their own good dropped piece after piece, all of which happily missed us and ended up crackling under-foot.

'Stop that! Stop that!' I shouted up at them.

'You're an eejit, but I love you, Hanvey.'

'I'm in the right place, but I'm glad you're here with me,' I replied.

'And the same goes for me too, Hanvey.'

Maggie took short, healthy puffs from a Benson and Hedges, held freely in slender flawless fingers, as a gentle breeze barely touched our skin and prepared itself for a busy summer in the fields and streets of Ulster.

I kicked a loose stone in front of me.

Coming to where it had rested she kicked it also, at the same time searching my eyes for approval before turning her head and blowing more of those perfect, fluffy rings into the air.

Her teeth laughed beautifully through thin, lifting smoke until I could see her face clearly again.

As we entered the Lower Garden the hospital towered above and behind us, so unbelievably big, like the Titanic - majestic, commanding, immovable, but home to us nevertheless.

Sitting down on a row of haphazardly arranged cement blocks I noticed a pair of black Rosary beads snake slowly from my right trouser pocket and gradually find their way to the ground.

Picking them up quickly with gleeful excitement she remarked, 'I didn't think that you were very religious.'

'Now Maggie, a person's religion is a very private thing. But I suppose you're right. I'm not terribly religious, but my parents are. Just like you.'

Carefully examining every bead on every decade with the delicacy of handling a butterfly, she asked, 'Where did you get them?'

'My father gave them to me before I left home to come here. He said they would keep me safe during life's journey, and so far they've done that.'

'He's right,' she answered, as she looked deeply into my eyes as if trying to emphasise the fact.

A group of twenty patients, accompanied by a nurse, were approaching, dancing and singing their way down the steep pathway which was the other entrance to the garden.

Donovan was doing his stuff on one of those small, tinny-sounding, transistor radios as everyone joined in, in perfect time.

The song was 'Mellow Yellow'.

The singing grew louder and came closer. 'I'm just mad about Saffron and Saffron's mad about me.'

On the word mad they purposely raised the level of their voices and shouted it out really loud, to let us know they weren't quite so mad as some people would have liked to believe.

'Hello, Nurse Hanvey. Hello Nurse Maguire,' they called in a jumble with one voice over-lapping the other, but Donovan sang on regardless.

'It's a lovely day, Nurse Hanvey,' said Mary, who had been a patient at Downshire for over forty years.

'Hello, Mary. It sure is one great day.'

'Do you like my new lipstick, Nurse?' asked Bridget.

'Look at my new shoes, Nurse,' pointed Annie.

'Is Nurse Maguire and you getting married, Nurse Hanvey?' asked Dorothy. Before I could reply she told me she hadn't taken her medicine, and said she loved Donovan.

'We are going to Beach House for our summer holidays. It's great out there,' she bubbled.

'Where are you going now?' I enquired.

'To the Sugar Bowl,' was the united reply.

Ruth was also a long-stay patient, known throughout the hospital for her tremendous ability, when it came to telling jokes. All of her yarns were in one way or another connected to the nursing profession, as if in some strange way this was her only means of striking back at a system which was kind to her, but which detained her against her will just the same.

'Would you like to hear a joke, Nurse?'

'I'd love to Ruth.'

'Right,' she smiled, 'An African patient walked into Doctor Dougal's office (Doctor Dougal was the Consultant Psychiatrist) with a parrot perched on his head. Doctor Dougal looked over his glasses and said, 'Yes, can I help you?' 'You can indeed,' replied the parrot, 'Would you mind getting this black head out of my foot?'

Roaring with uncontrollable laughter they moved away just as quickly as they had arrived, this time with Mick Jagger and the Rolling Stones belting it out across the airwaves.

The song being sung had been doing the rounds for over a year and was popular, especially within the confines of Downshire, 'Here it comes; here it comes; here comes my nineteenth nervous breakdown.'

Maggie was pulling her own Rosary in string-like movement from a warm, breast pocket, her finger and thumb gently trailing the silver crucifix upwards, until the end loop leaped to freedom and crashed softly onto her creaseless uniform lap.

Carefully lifting them, I kissed the 'sign of the cross'. Then, placing the crucifix against her lips I kissed her. With only our knees touching our eyes burned.

'Maggie Maguire, I'll always love you.'

'And I'll always love you too, Bobbie Hanvey.'

Taking the two sets of Rosary beads in both hands, I mixed and jumbled them up as a pipe-smoker might rub tobacco.

I felt this procedure would copper-fasten our love forever.

'THE DAY TRIP'

I had known a week earlier that the day trip to the seaside was on. This was one of the more enjoyable aspects of the nursing profession, when patients and staff would leave the hospital in early morning and seldom return before bedtime, which was usually around ten o'clock.

It was a day when the nearest hotel would be invaded, confectionery and ice cream shops swamped and a never ending supply of cigarettes laid on free-of-charge by the hospital staff.

On the morning of departure the atmosphere was electric.

Patients who normally rose with a little encouragement at seven, had been washed and dressed and walking up and down in anticipation from day break. Big Davy, The General, Mosie, Buns, The Butt and The Human Cannonball were a few of the boys preparing to make this the greatest day of their lives. Old Johnny Longstone sat expressionless in the chair below the budgies' cage gazing at a television which was still fast asleep, with no power and no programmes.

His isolation in the midst of thirty empty chairs pointing in as many different directions was total, yet his frail, lonely reflection on that dull, grey screen probably told him, and him alone, a story of what might have been, had Lady Luck dealt him a kinder hand.

Johnny had worked in radio during the nineteen forties and fifties and had a career which most people would 'die' for: unlimited expense accounts, foreign travel, mixing with the rich and famous and a beautiful home and family in Belfast's suburbia, completed a fairy-tale life style.

When a classic interview with a well known local clergyman went terribly wrong, he overnight gained the status of persona non grata and his talents were no long required.

On that far off day, as radio sets across the province warmed comfortable parlours with their vital weekly message, a dozy wasp suitably clad in its usual yellow and black striped pullover silently entered the studio. As with humans who were also approaching the end of their life span it seemed to spend more time walking than it did in flight.

Tiptoeing at speed and sporting the customary hump on its back, this little fellow soon gained unnoticed admission to the inside of Johnny's open-necked shirt.

As the Holy Reverend led the praises of all the things which were good in life and commented on the beautiful summer weather presently being sponsored by the Lord Jesus Christ, Johnny roared 'Fuck it,' as the wasp's lethal injection buried itself deeply in his bronzed suntanned chest.

Next morning he was told to pack his bags and go. His days at the microphone were over.

'Old hands', who had been nursing for a lifetime and who remembered Johnny being admitted to Downshire, recalled him being a proper gentleman, soft spoken with an English accent, which was neither here nor there, but quite pleasant just the same.

An outstanding conversationalist during his early days of hospitalisation, time saw him gradually regress to using mono-syllables when his wife finally left him, and her visits ceased.

After that period of cascading traumas all he would say to any question or suggestion was 'Fuck it.' No other words ever crossed his lips, although he must have known thousands.

'Its a lovely morning, Johnny.'

'Fuck it,' was his only reply.

'Are you going to Church today? The Reverend Brown is coming down from Belfast.' Without fail, each and every time his answer was the same.

Standing five feet four with a pencil-thin moustache he forever reminded me of Scottish accordion player Jimmy Shand. Johnny had a nasty little habit of creeping up on patients and staff when they least expected it, before letting fly with a lethal, hatchet-sharp fist. Hit or miss he always added 'Fuck it,' which had been his nickname for almost fifteen years.

Still this year's trip would be transformed beyond recognition from anything experienced before and the boys were rarin' to go.

For the first time in The Mental's long history, Male Forty-Seven would amalgamate with Female Thirty-Eight just for the day, and the patients agreed that this new programme of social interaction could only lead to better things. It was 8.20 am when the receptionist in the Front Hall telephoned the ward to inform us the excursion bus had arrived.

Big Cecil the Charge Nurse walked briskly from his office and stopped suddenly in the middle of the dayroom floor.

Thirty pairs of anxious eyes were agog and gazing at him. Ties of every shape and colour had been tightened, shoes polished to an army shine, and Brylcreem-laden heads combed in very style imaginable.

'Right boys,' commanded Big Cecil, 'The bus is here; grab your things and let's go.'

A loud cheer went up and almost immediately died down again.

Seconds later a solitary voice cheeped, 'Fuck it.' It was Johnny, of course.

'Shut him up, Nurse,' bellowed Big Davy, 'Sure he's nothin' only a dirty, foul-mouthed, fuckin' cunt.'

'Hammer the bastard and choke him.'

'When are we getting our dinner,' stormed John Joseph, eager to get in on the act.

'Now John Joseph, you're only after your breakfast. Don't worry. You'll get your dinner in the big hotel.'

'What about my tea, Nurse? What about my tea? I need my tea,' he panicked.

'You'll get your tea too, John Joseph,' I assured him.

Jimmy always wore a cap. In the ward, at work in the gardens or when fast asleep in bed, it never left his head.

Twenty years earlier when conditions in The Mental were more primitive and before medicine revolutionised treatment, Jimmy had been given a pre-frontal leucotomy. This was the worst cure imaginable for unpredictable behaviour. A drill, similar to the ones used on masonry, bored through the bone at the side of the temple, and clinically sterilised medical instruments probed their way around the brain, cutting and removing the offending parts which were then deemed responsible for his irrationality.

This procedure was regarded as hit and miss and was known to sometimes kill the personality.

In Jimmy's case it made him more loveable and docile but sharpened his already caustic sense of Ulster humour. His general demeanour was one of shell-like delicacy which gave the impression that if you should touch him he would disintegrate.

After the operation, his hair never grew again and a deep dent on the side of his forehead was living proof as to the point of entry.

The pain he endured during convalescence was to stay with him, because his description of the torment forever present was graphically described by his horrific account of the events at the time, as he remembered them.

New Student Nurses, prompted by the older hands would ask, 'Jimmy, what happened to your head?'

His answer never varied. The constancy of the same chilling string of words added to their authenticity and convinced us beyond any shadow of a doubt that whatever we heard was true.

'They shaved my head with a broken bottle and shoved a live dog up my arse,' was his condensed and teeth-rasping reply. As a description of pure, blue, naked pain I have never heard a more flesh crawling account.

Jimmy was now standing in his full frame of five feet eight in front of me, smiling and winking with his left eye at irregular intervals.

'Give me a fag, Nurse,' he wheezed, as he proceeded to deliver a mild threat from an organisation which had lain dormant since 1962.

'I'm the Secretary of the I.R.A.,' he warned, 'And if you don't give me a fag I'll blow up your wife.'

'But I haven't got a wife Jimmy,' I smiled.

'Then I'll blow up your mother,' he rattled.

'But my mother lives in the County Fermanagh,' I smirked.

'It doesn't matter where she lives. If I manage to get the message out she'll not be safe in China. I'm Secretary of the Irish Republican Army. Do you know how much money we have in the bank?'

'No Jimmy, I don't.'

'Four and eleven pence,' he grinned.

'Here's a fag Jimmy. The last thing this ward needs is an explosion. Now go with the rest of the boys to the bus.'

'Thanks, Nurse. You're lucky this time. Let's hope your luck holds out,' he concluded, walking off with the cigarette clenched in narrow lips, collar turned up and hands dug deep in long overcoat pockets, which like his cap was on him day and night.

As far as being Secretary of the I.R.A. was concerned, I wasn't so sure. There was no mention of it in his case notes, but from the way he spoke and swaggered I suppose it could very well, at one time have been possible.

Within a matter of minutes all of the patients fell into line and were soon eagerly seated in the bus beside an equal number of female patients.

'I see you have a new girlfriend, Johnny,' sparked Joe Mulligan, a Student Nurse from the County Tyrone. 'What would you do if you took her to the cinema?'

'Fuck it,' he responded, with a face void of any known emotion.

The bus was in an uproar as the Charge Nurse and Ward Sister once again counted and checked heads and finally took their seats. The key in the ignition turned. The old engine which had seen better days, spluttered and coughed and the big wheels started to roll.

We were on our way to Portrush.

'STILL ON THE BUS'

It was my luck to be seated beside Sister O'Flynn. She had originally come from the County Roscommon and was in her mid-to-late forties, or so it appeared to me at the time.

Ward Sisters had fearsome reputations and were looked upon by the junior nursing staff as being overbearing, frustrated and vicious. Constantly ruling with the iron fist, their names were forever being discussed and repeated like a litany of terror. It wasn't good news to be notified you were being transferred to one of their wards and the fear of going there provided me with many sleepless nights.

'Good morning, Nurse Hanvey,' she said stiffly.

'Good morning, Sister O'Flynn,' I smiled.

'You're making quite a name for yourself in Downshire,' she added.

'Is that so, Sister,' I answered, wondering how much she'd heard about my antics and how much she'd disapproved.

I don't know a lot about introductions but I did know her approach was straight from the psychology textbook.

If you want to put someone at ease when meeting them for the first time you simply say, 'Hello, I'm pleased to meet you. I've heard so many nice things about you.' On the other hand, if you want them to feel ill-at-ease your approach should be, 'Oh, hello, I've heard so many things about you.' They then begin to wonder what you've heard, if it was good or bad, and will probably go to the ends of the earth to find out what you know and who told you. This was Sister's approach.

'I hear you're living in the Nurses' Home, Nurse Hanvey.'

'Yes, I like it there, Sister,' I replied. 'It's so different from the County Fermanagh.'

'How is it different?' she asked.

'Well, in the Male Home I have a bath and hot water twenty-four hours a day. At home in Brookeborough I used to rig the garden hose up to the cold water tap in the scullery and pull it through the kitchen window out into the coal house. I'd throw the nozzle over a rafter and shower all summer long, but every time I'd take a shower my problem was always the same. My feet and ankles were black and japped by the coal so I had to fill the basin and wash them all over again. Still, those were great, happy days for me.

'The Male Home also has a fridge which is never allowed to go empty. I never saw one before I came to Downshire. All we had was a larder; a little square, green cage with tin sides, all drilled with thousands of tiny circular holes, only just big enough to allow the air to circulate through, and small enough to keep the flies out.'

'Yes I remember them,' she recalled. 'We had one as well.'

'So there you are now, Sister. Now you know what I'm talking about, but I bet you never showered in the coal.'

She gave no answer.

'Jesus, I shouldn't have said that,' I thought, and me supposed to show respect for authority.

'I'm sorry Sister. I shouldn't have said that,' I apologised.

'And so you shouldn't, Nurse Hanvey,' she coldly replied, but immediately asked me what other facilities I found in the Nurses' Home.

'My bed linen is changed every week and I get two clean towels every day. There's a washing machine, a telephone, central heating and a television, although my father recently bought one of those.

'When my money runs out Mr Sammy Stewart, who's very kind, keeps me floating from his petty cash box in the Wages Office until pay day. Only for him I couldn't afford to work here. We have a tennis court behind the Home and a Morgue to the side, so I think I have everything I need. Downshire sure is one great place.'

'Your mentioned the Morgue,' she echoed curiously.

'Yes, I did.'

'Why did you mention the tennis court and the Morgue in the same breath,' she sifted.

'No special reason, Sister. They're almost beside each other, that's all.'

'Do you go to post-mortems?' she bristled.

'As often as possible,' I smiled.

'Why?' she demanded.

'Well, my mate Billy and I know when there's going to be one because we see the hearse passing by,' I explained.

'But why do you go?' she persisted.

'Because it passes the time and anyway we enjoy seeing the young female nurses fainting when the bodies are opened up,' I added warmly.

'Oh yes, we enjoy it alright,' I revelled. 'Drownings, burnings, shootings, suicides, knifings, hangings, poisonings, road smashes, fallings from great heights. I think we've seen death from every cause and I suppose there's probably not much left to see.'

'Does it ever make you sick?'

'It did in the beginning, but it doesn't any more. I reckon we can get used to anything, Sister.'

Lighting a long cigarette she briefly looked at me before glancing away again and added, 'I'm not so sure about that.'

'Did you know Sister, that Protestants and Catholics have one thing in common?'

'And that's what?' she asked immediately, giving me the impression that no known comparisons existed.

'They all go to Heaven with their heads full of The Irish News.'

'Please get to the point and explain yourself, Nurse Hanvey.'

'Oh, O.K. Sister. As you know the Morgue Attendant reads The Irish News and it's his job to prepare the body for the pathologist. After he removes all the major organs such as the heart and lungs and dissects them, it's the Assistant's task to return them to the body. Usually they're poured into the cavity from a basin, but the brain, for whatever reason, is always put back into the skull. To prevent it from rattling about he packs the inside of the skull with The Irish News. So there you have it,' I concluded.

'Surely it's not normal to want to see that,' she ventured, as she reached into her broad uniform pocket for her cigarettes. She gave me one.

'It's part of the training, Sister - just part of the training.'

She then asked me if I'd mind taking down my guitar from the luggage rack and start a sing-song, which I did.

Songs popular at the time were 'Blowing in the Wind', 'The Universal Soldier', 'Colours', 'Mursheen Durkin', 'Fine Girl You Are' and 'The Leaving of Liverpool'.

I had just finished the last verse of 'Mr Tambourine Man' when Long Tommy leaned over me with his big, bony right hand fixed in the shape of a Colt 45. A straight, yellow, nicotine-stained finger trembled nervously only inches from Sister's left ear, as his narrowed lips made a smacking, popping sound every time his thumb moved forward.

Six 'shots' were fired in rapid succession into the side of Sister's carefully groomed head, and then, as if nothing had happened he turned quietly and walked slowly back to his seat.

'When's the post-mortem?' I laughed.

'What post-mortem?' she asked as if struggling to break away from a day dream.

'Your own,' I chuckled, before once again realising I was very much out of order, and not behaving quite like a Student Nurse should.

Pulling deeply on a fresh Benson and Hedges she slowly exhaled and calmly exclaimed, 'Oh,' as if paying me no attention.

Turning slowly and doing her best to face me in such a confined space, her turf brown, searching eyes adopted the stare of authority and her full lips prepared to move.

'Nurse Hanvey, during your training at the School of Nursing did Mr Kinsella or Mr Crangle ever advise you on how to properly address and speak to your Senior Nursing Staff? To show them the courtesy and due respect which their position deserves. Were you taught that, Nurse Hanvey?'

'I'm sorry Sister. Please forgive me. I was taught the proper procedure but I suppose I wrongly believed that differences in rank could be relaxed just for today because of the day trip.'

'Always remember, whilst on duty or off, you are a Nurse first and foremost and it would do well not to forget that fact. Remember, your ward reports, your behaviour and that includes your behaviour today, are all recorded and assessed and used when your Final Examinations are marked. So it is to your benefit and your benefit alone that you learn to present yourself in a more professional manner.'

'Jesus. She's one rotten, rank-pulling bastard,' I thought.

'I'm sorry Sister. Please forgive me. It won't happen again.'

'I sincerely hope not, Nurse Hanvey.'

'Jesus! Fuck! What a cunt,' I seethed. 'If only Long Tommy's gun had been real and blown her fuckin' head off.' Long Tommy hadn't a care in the world. Six foot seven in his bare feet he was one of the few patients at Downshire who amazed me to the point of bewilderment and fear.

Twenty years earlier, Tommy and some friends were packed into the front row of their local village cinema gaping wide-mouthed as 'Big John' fought it out with the Injuns to the bitter end.

During the final minutes of the film as the audience clutched the edges of their seats, Tommy produced an air rifle from a meal-bag, took careful aim and fired, hitting 'The Duke' right between the eyes. The screen gave a loud crack and split in two and local officers from the Royal Ulster Constabulary removed him pronto. The local judge declared he had been 'highly irresponsible' and the local newspaper gave him the classic headline 'Local Man Shoots John Wayne'. After that he was admitted to his local mental hospital and he'd been detained at Downshire ever since.

He loved watching cowboy films on television, but only if those same cowboys were chasing Indians. He hated movies about outlaws such as Jessie James and Billy the Kid, and couldn't understand why the Lone Ranger never shot Tonto.

During unending gun battles on the burning plains of Texas he'd slowly draw his imaginary six gun, which was anything but imaginary as far as he was concerned, and let fly at the screen.

Discharging the usual half dozen rounds he would then swing the barrel upright to his mouth and coolly blow away any remaining smoke with one short puff.

Rapidly reloading, he'd jump from his chair as if being bitten and eaten alive by a million fleas, pull up the corner of the large floor mat and quickly empty the 'chamber' at what I'll never know, before returning the covering to its former position.

Long Tommy had a body scientists would die for, but it always amazed me as to how it worked.

Few individuals alive had escaped the compulsion of masturbation at least sometime in their lives and Tommy was no exception.

So engrossed was he in these frequent exercises, he remained totally oblivious to any nursing or domestic staff who were forever walking past him in the course of their duty. Giving the odd curse or two, he always continued with his 'business' and the staff, in time also became blind to his not unnatural behaviour.

He always did it stark naked, while sitting on the edge of his bed. Ward maids would glide past with their mops and buckets pretending not to notice, but the part of the floor opposite to where he sat was always given more attention than the rest.

A female nurse once told me that female patients in their seventies also did it, which she said was part of their second childhood and she maintained was something associated with touch.

But Tommy was different from anyone I'd ever seen before and he really made my skin creep.

Two fully blown breasts decorated his chest like balloons on a Christmas tree, and as he gained momentum with a well practised right hand, his left continuously explored and caressed his massive mammaries.

As 'Vesuvius' erupted for the umpteenth time they slowly became less aggressive and wobbled to steadiness again, as a Chivers Jelly might do, just before it sets.

Then through frosted eyes of haze and glaze he calmly looked at me as if he had been interrupted while writing a letter. 'Oh, it's you Nurse. Make me a cup of tea.'

Long Tommy was seated in the back seat of the bus beside Cecil the Charge Nurse. Tommy point blankly refused to sit beside any female and knowing him it was easy to understand why. He didn't have to. It was a momentous occasion for patients who occupied a disturbed locked ward to have a day out.

A few years earlier some of the more forward looking staff headed by Chief Male Nurse Jack Lees had decided to throw open the gates and make the hospital more accessible to the community at large.

Open days and visits were organised and encouraged, and revolutionary more humane thinking became the norm. The efforts of this far-sighted nursing team proved most successful in breaking down the barriers associated with mental illness, and Downshire became a shining example to other institutions in the British Isles.

The hospital's former Victorian title of 'Down Lunatic Asylum' had long since been changed to Downshire Mental Hospital. A partially successful push to have it recognised as Downshire Psychiatric Hospital never really caught on, with people in the fairly large catchment area still referring to it as The Mental. This probably made some people feel superior, knowing the less fortunate within the walls were a useful yardstick with which outsiders could measure their own standing and success in society.

The bus was now snaking its way through Belfast's narrow streets as smiling, laughing, cheering faces beamed frantically at the 'normal' people walking here and there and going about their daily business, all of them oblivious to the happiness and sense of adventure held behind the perspex walls of that old Ulsterbus. On outings such as this, cursing by the patients was almost non-existent, yet back on the wards at rising time on ordinary days the language being released was vile. Today, the anger which promoted such profanity simply wasn't there.

At intervals which were more frequent than usual, young nurses would zig-zag up and down the aisle of the bus dishing out endless cigarettes to eager, hardened smokers. Chronically disturbed patients weren't allowed to carry their own and matches were totally forbidden.

It was during times like this I would talk to Sister about my studies and forthcoming exams and basically try and pick her brain on the finer points of mental nursing.

'Nurse Hanvey. Explain to me the difference between neurosis and psychosis.'

She would then proceed to tell me that the neurotic built castles in the air and the psychotic was the fellow who moved in and lived in them. So in many ways it was much better being a neurotic.

'Are you studying much, Nurse Hanvey?'

'Yes, a bit Sister. Not as much as I should, but I'll cram it in in the weeks before the exam,' I hoped.

'Sometimes cramming it in simply doesn't work. How many girlfriends have you got now?' was a question which I thought had little to do with exams, but she then advised me before I could answer, that too much recreation didn't fit into the pattern of success in nursing. After this statement I realised that everything could be connected to nursing.

'Are you singing much on radio now, Nurse Hanvey?' she enquired.

'Not much. Just a little. The programme producer Maurice Leitch is going to England to concentrate on writing,' I explained.

'Get this unholy slut off me. That painted whore of Babylon.'

It was Big Andy. One of the female patients had sat down on his knee and put her arm around his neck. He was totally repelled. He didn't like it at all.

'Get her fuckin' off me, Nurse. I wouldn't ride the bitch even if she wanted paid in Free-State money. Get her off to fuck, Nurse before I have a heart attack.' The Charge promptly removed her. Big Andy clasped his two chubby, but well-worked hands over his bulging, rotund belly and once again immediately adopted the pose of complete contentment.

Big Andy was a merchant seaman and had sailed everywhere on the face of the globe where he could find water. During the early nineteen fifties he caught the 'clap' in Central America and had received treatment by 'hot needle'.

'Bobbie,' he emphasised, 'Those black heathen bastards of Doctors, those wee fuckers tried to kill me and I'd swear they were smiling while they did it. They rammed a burning hot needle up my penis and closed it over. They then pushed a button and the needle opened up inside my prick like an umbrella and they pulled it out again. The pain was unbearable.'

Since then he never spoke to or looked at a woman, insisting they were all whores. 'But Catholic whores are the worst,' he would add.

Speaking with one of the richest, most listenable Ulster accents I'd ever heard he continued, 'They would shag like dogs - give you the clap and then go and torment the Priest in Confession with all the dirty details. They are all scum,' he persisted, 'And their depravity knows no ends.'

It was Andy's job on my first day in 'his' ward, to take me out to the garden with the patients' work group. The Charge had appointed him to show me the ropes.

Going down the back steps he pointed to a patient in his early thirties. Whatever madness really was, and I wasn't so sure, I figured this had to be it - perpetual motion - not one second of stillness. With the force of a rogue elephant he pounded up and down in an area specially sealed off just for him.

Constantly waving his arms in the air and with clapping hands and flicking fingers he roared like a bull. Heavily built with the strength of steel, his feet hammered the ground and the earth echoed and shook. Between roars he would chant, 'Ja Ja, Ha Ha, Ga Ga, Ya Ya, La La, Ma Ma, Da Da.

'Do you see him?' asked Andy seriously.

'Yes,' I quavered, thinking how could I miss him, but also putting a brave face on it at the same time and hoping the wire fence held.

'Well Nurse,' continued Andy, 'Before he ended up in here he was a Bank Manager, so you have to be careful in The Mental and look after your body, Bobbie. Treat it as you would a shrine and it will look after you.'

Three times daily Big Andy would announce he was going for a C.B. which was his code for a cold bath, and three times a day with the energy of a whale he would splash in a tub so full the water rolled over the edge in tidal waves and ran across the black and white, square-tiled floor. One night in winter as all the patients and staff sat engrossed watching television someone in the far corner of the ward let an almighty fart.

'Thar she blows, Nurse,' smiled Andy, 'Did you hear that prize-winner? Grab your harpoons my hearties.'

The humour now building up in the dayroom was quickly putting the TV in the shade.

'Tell him to fuck up, Nurse. He's mad. I want to see the Queen on the box,' bellowed Big Davy.

'Nurse, tell the stupid fucker the only time he'll see Her Majesty on that fuckin' television is at Christmas and close-down, and since he'll be in bed from ten o'clock then it's Christmas or nothin'. The pathetic peasant,' grated Andy.

Before Big Davy could retaliate a second 'blast' sounded from roughly the same location.

'Did you hear that, Nurse? There it goes again. That bastard will shite himself and then we'll all be suffocated,' complained Andy.

'It's only a fart,' chuckled John Joseph as he continued to waltz haphazardly between lines of seated patients and glide past the television at twenty second intervals, managing to annoy the entire gathering.

'No, it's not a fart, that's the Oirish love call,' quipped Andy in a poor imitation of a Free-State accent. 'Their arses think their throats are cut. No decorum, no breeding - they're just fuckin' animals. Do you see those bastards? They'd sell their arses for sixpence,' he stormed. 'Let me out of here before I choke. I'm going for a C.B. Could you get me a towel, please, Nurse?'
'Sure Andy. Right now?'

'Right now. Thank you Bobbie.'

Andy gave me a call card he picked up in a Havana night club in the days before Castro moved in and wiped out prostitution. Printed on both sides in English and Spanish it depicted a scantily-clad beautiful Latin girl lying in the 'missionary' position.

He had been there alright and he'd seen it all.

His favourite hymn, 'When the roll is called up yonder' was now being belted out by a mixed choir of some fifty mobile voices, with the big man taking the lead and conducting the lesser mortals, as he saw them, with perfect grace and poise.

Sister was eating the cigarettes and matching me one for one.

'Are you still going out with Nurse Maguire?' she queried.

'Aye, indeed I am. She's coming back from holidays on Monday. I just can't wait to see her,' I eagerly replied.

'I suppose you love her,' she shot.

'I do indeed. Maggie is a good person and a great Nurse,' I said defensively.

'Oh, she's a good nurse alright,' jibed Sister. 'Sing another song,' she ordered.

It was approaching ten o'clock and the early rising had at last begun to cast a temporary shadow on the now sedate proceedings. Throats and limbs were being rested and only Andy seemed anxious that the momentum should be maintained.

Standing upright, his broad belly touching seats to his left and right he commanded, 'Right, Nurse Hanvey, strike the chord of B.'

'Is that B flat Andy?'

'There's only one B Nurse and this one's in the key of B Special,' he joked. Let's see if we can inject some life and drive, some good old-time religion into this band of pitiless heathens. You all know it, for God knows I've sung it a thousand times for you. The words are 'What a friend we have in Jesus'. Did you hear that, you dozy bastards? What a friend we have in Jesus.'

Old Harry was standing behind him carefully examining each and every word he uttered. 'Jesus, Jesus, Jesus,' he repeated, 'What a fr, fr, fr, what a, a friend ... What a friend we ... We have a friend .... What a friend we have in, in, in ...... In Jes ...... In Jes ...... Jesus, in J-E-A-S-U-S. Jesus. What a friend we have in Jesus. Give us a fag Nurse.'

'Don't mind him Nurse. He's totally and permanently insane. That poor bastard is so fucked up his mother wouldn't know him. Now brethren, let's commence our little timely tribute to the Lord Jesus Christ.'

Within seconds every voice on the bus was joining in. Some in front and some behind, but all doing as best they could and thoroughly enjoying themselves.

Harry was interspersing powerful pulls on his cigarette with more close analysis of Andy's words. 'What a friend we have ..... We have ..... We have a friend ..... A friend ..... A friend in Jesus. What a friend .... A F-R-I-E-N-D we have. What a friend we have in Jesus. J-E-A-S-U-S.'

'THE BIG HOTEL'

The big hotel looked like a henhouse when compared to the sprawling chateau that was Downshire but one thing the hotel did have which the hospital did not, and it was about to present more than a few problems, was the claustrophobic, four-sectioned, revolving glass door. The boys were all now marching straight towards it and there was no way of stopping them.

'What is it?' cheered John Joseph with glee. 'It's a ... it's a whirligig, it's a whirligig,' he babbled.

'Don't even bother to consider answering that Nurse. If you told the poor bastard he wouldn't believe you anyway,' advised Big Andy.

Big Andy was jammed solid in one of the glass triangles, as tight as a tinned sardine. In the next compartment, pushing and shoving and trying in vain to get it to move was John Joseph and Big Davy. Andy's twenty stones, however, proved too much for such a delicate invention and it stubbornly refused to budge.

The hotel manager, an efficient, nervous looking man in his mid-fifties, waved frantically through the window, and pointed anxiously to another door further along the building where presumably he would prefer us to make our entrance.

John Joseph, who hated enclosed spaces of any kind, was red-faced, fat and furious and was hitting the see-through partition with his fists, feet and head. His shock at being captured by such a thing probably explained his verbal silence.

Andy stood erect and motionless, looking upwards and praying for a miracle which hopefully would get things on the move again. Whenever trouble visited him his ready remedy was prayer and meditation. His pattern never varied.

Shouting for all he was worth Big Davy was beginning to panic and started punching John Joseph with short, right jabs to the small of his back. He simply had no room to hit him harder.

Columns of hotel staff and guests lined up on the inside, staring wildly in amazement at such an unusual commotion. On the outside, forty patients and nurses gazed across the divide into no-man's land.

His moment of prayer completed Big Andy edged forward slightly, his massive frame grazing the circular brass wall like ice grating along the side of the Titanic.

Feeling movement and obviously believing they were going to be catapulted into oblivion, John Joseph and Big Davy began to push frantically in the opposite direction. Thumping, banging, flailing and finally cursing, they were quickly ejected back to where they'd started from, pulling Andy out after them in the process and forcing him to keep running for a short distance, in order to maintain his balance.

The staff and guests on the inside applauded and we cheered.

'Well to hell with that for a contraption,' laughed Andy, 'I thought I was in there for life. The biggest whore in Havana wouldn't get me back into that kip-shop.'

'It's not funny, it's not funny,' whinged John Joseph who was jumping towards me in anger and pointing at Big Davy.

'He hit me, Nurse, he hit me. That bastard hit me in that .. that .. green-house! I'm not going to get in there again. I'm going home, I'm going home.'

'I didn't fuckin' touch him,' insisted Big Davy, who never admitted to anything.

'Did you take your dinner, Davy?'

'What fuckin' dinner?' would be his never changing reply.

By this time, the manager was approaching, carefully edging his way through the happy gathering and trying hard to give the impression he wasn't frightened when we all knew only too well he was.

'Can I help you, Sir? I'm Mr Turner,' he said to Charge Nurse Cecil.

'Indeed you can, we're on a trip from Downshire and we're very hungry.'

Everyone in Northern Ireland had heard about Downshire so there was no need to elaborate.

Smiling wildly and showing many stumps of well-ground teeth, John Joseph demanded 'I want Irish Stew and fried eggs and bacon and cabbage, and jelly and tea too!"

Mr Turner gave Cecil a puzzled, searching look as if to say, 'Does he really want all that, or does he know what he's talking about?'

'Yes, give him all he wants, this is his day out,' replied Cecil.

Mickey Mooney was seven feet tall and always licked his lips, even between meals. The very mention of food sent him running in the direction of the canteen. As the other patients finished their courses, Mickey would sit watching the bowl of soup, the dinner and the dessert. The minute his cup of tea was placed before him he'd shout, 'Bowl' and as soon as the domestic had answered his request the soup, dinner, dessert and tea were all emptied into it and stirred up.

'Why do you eat like that?' I would ask.

'That's the way it ends up in the stomach Nurse, so why give my stomach extra work when I can do it first,' he would laugh.

It seemed to make some sense to me, but I never tried it. I was too afraid.

Not daring to risk any more 'seizures' in the revolving door, Cecil and the manager led the way to the other opening, some twenty yards away.

On entering the plush foyer the first person we saw, standing in the middle of a line of tourists, and smiling his head off, was John Joseph.

'I did it Nurse, I did it,' he beamed.

The tourists looked at one another, and then at John Joseph, and then at us.

'You did what?' asked Cecil with a knowing grin.

'I spun through the glass-house. I did it! It worked!!' He was delighted.

'Good going,' replied Cecil. 'Well done.'

John Joseph had broken away from the main party and made a second attempt and I admired his determination - especially after being so frightened the first time.

Deep, red carpet, the type which invites you to lie down on it, expanded to every corner and corridor, as far as the eye could see, as two complicated, but ornate chandeliers swayed ever so gently, giving off just enough light and no more.

'I wish Christmas would hurry up,' I thought.

Bouncing Jeffrey had worked in circuses and shows all over Ireland as 'The Rubber Man', doubling as a rocket when he played his other role of 'The Human Cannonball'. He had also ridden the wall of death and too many falls had probably contributed to his present condition.

With the poise and grace of a ringmaster, Jeffrey commanded the attention of the entire gathering by stepping forward and announcing, in a clear, resounding circus voice, 'Ladies and gentlemen, for your entertainment tonight, from the darkest forests of coldest Russia, flown in at tremendous expense, for tonight, and one night only, I give you, for the first time in Ireland, Bouncing Jeffrey, The Rubber Man.'

Going quickly into his never forgotten routine, hands nimbly replaced feet, as he tumbled, cartwheeled and rolled, inches from the encircled throng, knocking the occasional cigarette from astonished lips with flashing, flying feet.

For a man of fifty plus, his act of years ago was still intact and honed to perfection. On his final revolution a beautifully arched, salmonlike back bowed, as he landed lightly in the upright position.

Tourists and hotel staff applauded wildly as they searched each others faces for obvious signs of approval - whether through sheer enjoyment or deadly fear, I just wasn't sure. My father always maintained, and I fully agreed with him, that applause was one of three things, Faith, Hope or Charity.

On the strength of Jeffrey's superb performance the patients moved speedily amongst the residents, 'tapping' them for cigarettes and absorbing whatever apparent happiness they could find.

'I want my tea now,' coaxed John Joseph.

'You're getting your dinner first, now relax,' I assured him.

'I don't want to relax, Nurse. I want my tea, I want my tea now. If I don't get my tea I'll wreck the house.'

I knew he wouldn't, and once again he soon settled down.

Robert Morgan never spoke unless spoken to, but being a compulsive reader had a terrific command of the English language. Fed up with the depressing sameness of his job as a fitter in the shipyard, he moved to the other side of town and opened up 'shop' - as a doctor. He had no qualifications, but having read all the relevant medical books and with a brass name plate, carefully inscribed by a friend in the metal department he soon enjoyed the comforts of a new and more lucrative social standing. This was in 1948. Two years later, the police stumbled onto his scheme and he eventually ended up in Downshire, where he once again became known as 'The Doctor'. Six or eight feet to my left, Robert was busy introducing himself to an American tourist.

'Good morning, Madam, I'm Doctor Morgan, Psychiatrist. Just out for the day to keep an eye on the patients, and so far, so good.'

'I'm pleased to meet you Doctor,' she smiled, through a mouthful of carefully manicured teeth. 'I'm Dorothy Silverstein, and I simply adore your country. It's so beautiful. Makes a pleasant change from Boston.'

'Been to any good tea parties lately,' he teased.

'If my memory serves me right, and I can't be sure, I think the last 'dish' of tea I had was in seventeen seventy-three,' she laughed, appreciating his knowledge of American history.

'And what's your profession Dorothy, apart from being a very fine historian,' he probed with humour.

'I'm a simple housewife, Doctor.'

'Call me Robert,' he purred.

'Thank you Robert, that's less formal. My husband was a Company Director but he died last Fall and my sons insisted I came to Ireland on vacation, so here I am,' she shrugged.

'I'm really sorry to hear that Dorothy, I hope he didn't suffer too much in his final days.'

'The crafty bastard,' I thought. Here she was, falling for it hook, line and sinker, or perhaps she was desperate and had little choice.

'No, it was a massive heart attack. He never knew what hit him. Still my two boys are carrying on the business and things are going very well,' she explained.

Realising I was within ear-shot, Robert gently put his hand to the small of her back and deep in conversation, slowly manoeuvred her towards the bar.

'Excuse me Doctor,' I fawned. 'May I speak to you a moment?'

Robert stepped up to me and spoke loudly, 'Yes indeed Nurse Hanvey how may I help you?'

Discreetly lowering my voice I warned Robert not to leave the hotel.

'Oh no Nurse, I shall be available of course, should any emergency arise.' Dismissing me with a friendly smile and dismissive wave of his hand he rejoined Dorothy, explaining that the nurses relied heavily on his expertise.

'Now, that that problem's solved, how about a drink? You will allow me to buy a beautiful lady such as yourself a drink,' he charmed, at the same time relieved at not being exposed.

'Oh, why not,' she revelled, 'I'll have a gin and tonic.'

'A gin and tonic for the lady and a double scotch, bartender,' he beamed. Frantically searching his inside and then his outside pockets he finally threw his hands up in amazement before hitting them off his thighs, 'Gosh Dorothy, I'm terribly sorry. I seem to have left my wallet in the car. I can't leave the hotel in case the nurses need my help and I don't like approaching them for money. Let's see if the Charge Nurse is about. He'll help.'

'You'll do no such thing, Doctor. Sorry - Robert. Please allow me,' she insisted as she opened her purse and told him to help himself.

'Oh no Dorothy, I couldn't possibly. Such a trusting lady.'

'Gee Robert, if I can't trust a doctor who can I trust?' As she proffered the roll of bills he delicately withdrew four crisp, brand new, Ulster Bank twenty pound notes, promising to return them later in the day. I couldn't believe my eyes but kept on watching just the same.

Within seconds the friendly barman had set up the drinks on a highly varnished spotless counter and Robert, having folded one of the notes in four, deftly pushed it between his first two fingers.

'Keep the change,' he winked confidently.

'Thank you very much Sir,' returned the barman, 'You're very kind.'

'Not a bit,' dismissed Robert in a stiff, upper-crust but most impressive accent.

'A nice guy Gordon, he always looks after me when I visit my clinics in the area,' he spoofed.

Raising her glass to meet his, she smiled warmly.

'Good health Dorothy, and coming from a doctor you'll appreciate that's very good advice indeed.'

'Robert, I believe you kissed the Blarney Stone.'

'No Dorothy, I swallowed it,' he chuckled.

Fifteen minutes later we were seated in the main dining hall surrounded by a cluster of well-tanned, happy summer faces. Robert was seated directly to my left and Dorothy and a group of American friends sat at the table behind us by the large bay window overlooking the sea.

During the soup a powerful voice which mimicked the Reverend Ian Paisley boomed and stressed.

'Do youse sinners believe in the Lord Jesus Christ? Have youse committed any untold acts of fornication today? If youse have, you'd better fall on your knees in the sight of God and repent; I said repent friends, before it's too late. I don't care if you're in and out or up and out, brown and white or black and white; you can be Chinese, Japanese, Cantonese or Vietnamese. I don't care, friends, if your allegiance is to the White House, The House of Representatives or the coal house; I tell you now you stand naked today before your Maker, cowering like fools waiting on the death sentence to be passed. Are you prepared for the final chapter, friends, before you're delivered to the arse-burning pains of Hell? Tell me friends, are you ready?

Two male nurses apologised to Dorothy and her friends before marching the 'Reverend Eddie' back to his dinner.

'Let me go, you Fenian rabble,' he shouted struggling half-heartedly to break free.

'These Papists are trying to silence God's man in Ulster, and if they think for one minute they're going to gag God's man and prevent him from spreading the word of the Lord Jesus Christ then I've got news for them. They might as well be trying to stop the Niagara Falls with a pitchfork.'

'What an orator,' I thought. 'He's fuckin' brilliant,' but reminding myself that when one incident like this happens it's usually followed by another, and sure enough it was.

Big Davy gathered speed as he charged across the floor to a table which was occupied by female patients. Creeping up behind the stoutest, he quickly cupped her breasts with two brawny, nicotined hands.

'Yo, Yo, Yo, Yo,' chanted Davy with a fat smile at least half a mile wide.

Alice bounced to her feet in hysterics.

'Sister O'Flynn, he grabbed my diddies. He fuckin' hurt my diddies, the dirty oul' bastard.'

Big Davy was unceremoniously led back to his table, roaring at the top of his voice.

'I never fuckin' touched her diddies; she's a lying bitch. Diddies, diddies, diddies! All I ever fuckin' hear is diddies, diddies, diddies! What the hell do I want with diddies?' he finished, exhausted, before collapsing back in his chair.

'Good answer Davy,' I thought. 'Well done.'

The female tourists were disgusted - or so it appeared at the time.

As desserts were being attacked with hefty spoons and an orchestra of hinged elbows, I casually glanced to my left where my worst fears were realised. I had lost a patient, my first, and this was the worst fate which could possibly befall a psychiatric nurse.

Walking briskly to the next table I told the Charge Nurse that Robert was missing. In turn, he moved toward the nearest waiter, 'Excuse me, we're a patient short, did you see a man of five feet nine in a tweed jacket and spotted dickie-bow tie?'

'With light grey slacks and patent black shoes,' he replied.

'Yes, that's him, where did he go?' asked Cecil.

'He's with Mrs Silverstein. They've gone to her room,' as he pointed in the direction of upstairs.

'Christ,' replied Cecil, 'Take me there.'

Scanning the dining area, I soon discovered that her seat, like Robert's, was empty.

'He's riding her,' cheered John Joseph, who along with half a dozen of his comrades had now joined the posse.

'He is, my fanny,' beamed Big Andy. Andy had told us in furtherance of our education that backsides were called fannies in America. When asked what they called fannies out there his reply was, 'The same as they call them here.'

Big Cecil tore up the stairs behind the waiter. Through countless corridors of carpets we surged until the rush stopped abruptly outside the door of room 429.

The door of room 429 was identical to all the others but the deafening sound of classical music beating its way through wood and mortar told us a party was in progress.

'Turn it down,' bellowed Davy, pulling his coat over his head in an effort to close out the din.

'Ah Beethoven's Ninth,' enthused Andy as he hummed along with the Berlin Philharmonic, conducting every instrument to perfection with the tip of his 2B pencil.

'I love Choppin',' echoed John Joseph, unable to get his tongue around Chopin.

'Ignore him Nurse,' laughed Big Andy, 'The only thing that poor bastard will ever chop is sticks.'

The Charge's fist kept up a steady, dull, thud, thud, thud in the middle of the panel just below the numbers 429.

'He's at her,' chirped John Joseph, 'He's at her, Nurse.'

Seconds after the music ceased a small lady, liberally sprinkled with gold and diamonds appeared in a full-length, towelled, dressing gown. 'Can I help you Sir?' she gleamed.

'I am looking for Doctor Morgan and I believe he's with you,' enquired Cecil.

'I'm here Cecil,' called Robert from within, 'Please enter Nurse and bring the boys with you.'

I'd never seen such luxury before. This hotel had to be six star, at least. Drinks cabinet, built-in wardrobes, crystal chandeliers and over in the corner at a darkened table for two, sat the bould Robert smoking a big cigar and politely sipping from a glass of Napoleon brandy.

A loaded chess-board sat proudly in front of him. To his right, a stack of ten pound notes left me in no doubt they'd been playing for money and he was winning.

'Beautiful holiday weather boys,' twanged Robert as he casually blew smoke upwards, over a perfectly planned and extended lower lip.

'Fuck it,' cried a voice from the crowd.

Cecil grinned his legendary grin, unconsciously stretching it from ear to ear. Looking at his watch he then directed his gaze towards the corner, and Robert.

'Well Doctor, time ticketh away and if we're going to see the shops and take a dander round the town we'd better make tracks, and anyway I'd like you to have a look at John Joseph. He hasn't been feeling too well.'

'Certainly Cecil, a brilliant idea. Just wait until I put on my jacket.'

'I'm not lettin' him near me. There's nothin' wrong with me. He was at her Nurse. Look! The bed's wrecked, he was at her. He's mad! I'm not lettin' him near me, he's sufferin' from a multitude of disarranged ideas and inflicted with a mass inferiority complex too!'

'Tut, tut, now now, John Joseph take it easy,' calmed the Doctor. 'Sorry I have to go Dorothy, duty calls. I'll be in touch.' As he spoke to Dorothy their eyes met, but his right hand which appeared to have a mind of its own, quickly scooped the pile of notes and buried them deeply in his hip-pocket.

'He's fuckin' stole the money,' snarled Big Davy.

'I don't think a man in your position needs to take money from a lady visiting our country for the first time,' cautioned Cecil.

'Of course you're right Nurse,' agreed Robert as he placed the money back firmly on the table.

'No please take it,' demanded Dorothy as she crossed the floor and gave it back to him. 'You won it fair and square, please take it,' she insisted.

'No thank you Dorothy. Buy yourself a new dress on me, as a memento of an unforgettable afternoon.'

Kissing her on the cheek and apologising for the interruption, Robert took her hands in his and said, 'Goodbye lovely lady.'

Downstairs in the bar, Cecil ordered orange juice for the company. Half an hour later, as glasses were constantly being refilled and cigarettes being replaced, Big Davy staggered across the floor singing at the top of his voice. The words of Danny Boy had been changed to 'Davy Boy' and sounded just as good, if not better than the original. Hacking hiccups ensured Davy's lyrics overlapped those of the gathering, but the singing continued regardless and no-one seemed to notice. As every voice reached the point of delirious crescendo a sudden, deafening silence filled the room, as an empty Napoleon brandy bottle which wasn't jammed tight enough in Davy's pocket, tipped out and clunked dangerously onto the highly polished, wooden floor. Rolling even and long like a 'brattle' of thunder it finally stopped at the base of the bar counter with every eye in the room quietly following its progress. It was the very same bottle I'd seen in Dorothy's room a short time earlier.

'Davy, where did you get that bottle?' asked Cecil.

'What fuckin' bottle? I didn't see no bottle,' he snarled.
'He stole it, he stole it off the oul' doll,' persisted John Joseph.

'I didn't 'stale' no fuckin' bottle,' roared Davy, as he took one almighty swing, catching John Joseph on the point of the chin and knocking him stone cold to the floor. With his balance already gone, Davy made a few perfect revolutions before ending up on top of his comrade who was already fast asleep.

The remainder of the day was relaxing and without major incident, as we demolished ice cream and sweets and lay on the beach in eighty degrees of sheer bliss. All patients had donned broad straw hats because their main drug Largactil, whilst being a powerful 'calmer downer' made the skin super-sensitive to the sun's rays and they would easily have fried without this protection.

After tea, at eight o'clock Cecil stood in the middle of the foyer and announced it was time to board the bus and head for home.

A big cheer went up and died down again. A solitary voice hidden in the crowd quietly exclaimed, 'Fuck it.'

Almost, but not quite the end to a perfect day.

'COMING HOME'

The evening sun struggled to make this the longest day of the year, but it found the going just that little bit too hard.

Twin rows of overhead seat lights bathed us with their sallow softness and grew brighter, only to fade again, as the engine coughed and revved in preparation for the long journey home. Behind us, an ocean of dying crimson spread across the sky like a purple vestment, as young Student Nurses dished out pocketful after pocketful of cigarettes to some of the most hardened smokers in Downshire. Fifty transistor radios tuned to as many different stations were pressed to the sides of happy, sleepy heads grasping for enjoyment with their last ounces of rapidly, flagging energy.

Even Big Andy sat motionless with hands clasped and eyes closed, deep in prayer. There would be little singing, if any, done tonight.

'That - that - that fu ...., he stole my rock and took a bite out of it. He - he took a bite of it, Nurse,' stammered John Joseph.

'Give him back his bar of rock and settle down,' ordered Cecil the Charge.

Cecil was the toughest Nurse to work for in the entire hospital. With him, patient-care was the main priority and he made us toe the line. We dreaded being sent to his ward, but in time we grew to like him and he soon earned our respect.

'Did you enjoy your day, Nurse Hanvey?'

'Yes,' Sister. 'Very much, thank you.'

'Do you not think you were a bit lax in letting Robert Morgan escape with the American woman?' she probed.

'He wasn't going anywhere, he was only enjoying himself, I can't see what all the fuss was about. Anyway, the Charge Nurse seems to think it's over and done with, so that's good enough for me,' I replied, angry and peeved at her latest onslaught.

'How dare you speak to me in that tone, Nurse Hanvey. Have you no respect whatsoever for authority? I'll make sure your current behaviour reflects in your marks for your final examinations,' she stormed.

'You do what you have to do Sister, but I think you are being extremely unfair,' I snapped.

'Nurse Hanvey, what you think counts for nothing and don't you ever forget it,' she fumed.

I didn't answer. The next words spoken came an hour later when an unmerciful thump almost demolished the side of my ribcage as her elbow dug me swift and deep.

'I see you are looking after your patients as you were taught in Training School,' she said sarcastically.

'Jesus, you scared me! I'm sorry Sister. I'm very tired and I must have dozed off. I promise it won't happen again.'

'She's one lousy psycho bastard,' I seethed.

'Sleeping on the job, Nurse; sleeping on the job cannot and will not be tolerated. I will be reporting you to your Unit Officer tomorrow.'

'You can tell him tonight for all I care,' I countered, no longer willing or able to take any more of her aggression.

'Nurse Hanvey! Would you mind repeating, slowly and clearly, what you've just said to me,' she intoned.

'Please forgive me Sister, I'm sorry. I had a few Bacardis back at the hotel and Bacardi always has a strange effect on me. It makes me anti-social. I'm not normally like this.'

'Ah. Drinking on duty as well, Nurse Hanvey! I'm afraid this will go very much against you in your Ward Report, and I intend to see it does,' she promised.

A good fifteen minutes passed and she never spoke a word. Most of the patients were now fast asleep and snoring their heads off. Constantly fighting to stay awake myself, I thought I was dreaming as her face drifted closer and touched my shoulder.

Looking at me now in a way which was completely out of character for someone of her rank, she smiled as I hadn't seen her smile before, and it was quite beautiful. It also disturbed me.

Desperately, I tried to figure out exactly what was going on.

Beauty was a quality I'd never recognised in Sister O'Flynn. In fact, her more than generous build led some female staff to christen her with two nicknames; 'Size Eighteen' and 'Click of the Heels'. Being tall, regimental and a stickler for discipline, but with more than a little femininity, 'Click of the Heels' painted disturbing images of concentration camp commandants and torture, but she was widely recognised as a first class Nurse. The male staff simply referred to her as 'Mighty Tits', and I had no need to wonder why.

Gazing at me in a playful way and smiling broadly with her lips closed, she tucked her chin tightly against her chest and with clipped, razor sharp diction said, 'And he huffed ... and he puffed ... and he blew the house down.' Her long fingers tickled me in the ribs as I remembered my mother doing when I was a child.

'What's going on here?' I asked myself. Here I was, tired, exhausted and brow-beaten by this psycho and all she could fucking do was recite nursery rhymes.

The soft, deceptive glow from the yellow lighting played tricks with my eyes and no matter how many times I tried to focus on reality, she appeared more attractive than the minute before, leaving me in a state of wild confusion.

'I think the patients are ready for another sing-song, Nurse Hanvey. Would you mind taking down your guitar and singing for us?'

102

'Oh, so it's 'us' now, is it?' I mimicked. 'O.K., Sister I'll do it!'

'That's the attitude, Nurse Hanvey. I'll make a Nurse of you yet,' she smiled.

During the second verse of 'The Leaving of Liverpool' with every voice on the bus raised, including Cecil's, something caught my attention which caused me to gaze in disbelief. I was sure, then I wasn't, so I looked again to try and convince myself I wasn't imagining things.

Her uniform seemed to be getting shorter and was already three inches above her knees. Perhaps it happened, I told myself, when she had sat down and it had just ended up like that, or maybe it had been that way all along and I simply didn't notice.

Some men can instinctively read female body language but I wasn't born with such a gift. I always had to be certain before I made a move; in fact I almost wanted it in writing.

Did her uniform end up as it did by accident, or was she purposely engineering this situation?

With no space whatsoever between us, I moved even closer until the heat of her body penetrated my clothes like a bowie-knife. She was approaching boiling point. Nervously stroking her palm I searched for a reaction. None came.

Soft smooth thighs lay moored in silence as my fingers commenced their long, slow journey. Her skin burned back at me as if in revenge but she never flinched.

'Why am I doing this?' I asked myself in wonder. She had given me a terrible day and made my life a misery. It was so obvious she disliked me intensely, but there was something powerful about her that was drawing me. Maybe it was her rank or maybe I longed for an easier passage through to my final exams. Whatever it was, I didn't know. Like being in a desert with no signposts I was stumbling blindly not knowing what I was going to find.

Minutes later my fingers had reached their destination. Their journey had ended and she appeared to be fast asleep.

'Jesus,' I thought, 'What if she really is asleep and wakens up to find me doing this? I'd be accused of 'attempted interference with a sleeping Ward Sister' or of 'tampering with authority'.' There was no greater crime in the book than meddling with the comatose. I would surely fry. The judge would throw the book at me. In fact I could picture him leaning on his bench in disgust and peering over his horn-rimmed glasses before sending me down for twenty years.

It didn't matter what the exact title for the crime I was presently committing was but he would have half a dozen legal terms for it. An obvious one would be 'behaviour likely to lead to a breach of the peace'. I would be sacked in disgrace from Nursing and would probably be given the nickname 'Rob the Dead'.

My finger, which had no such worries about legal terminology, was moist and trembling, keeping up a steady, even rhythm.

Her knees were now lax and pliable as my hand fought for more room.

Her thighs swung open like a well-oiled door and with eye-lids closed tighter than a window blind, perfect teeth bit randomly, on a full bottom lip.

Staff and patients were bawling 'The Yellow Submarine' when her muscles tightened in racking spasm and nearly pulled my hand off, as if in the throes of an epileptic fit, causing her legs to go rigid and her feet to disappear underneath the seat in front.

Her eyes glazed, hazed and disturbed searched vainly for something, but appeared lost and out of control.

Her previous dignified composure was long gone as I maintained the momentum and kept the pressure on. Her head moved in ratchet fashion, ever so slowly, each 'click' bringing it forward and outwards from the seat. She had arrived at the end of her 'journey' with beads of fresh sweat resting and streaking a water-laden face.

'What have you been doing to me, Nurse Hanvey? I must have been dreaming,' she sighed, settling back into the relaxed position.

'Now I'm for it,' I thought.
'I couldn't help it Sister. Please forgive me,' I said hoarsely. I was about to say it wouldn't happen again, but refrained in case I annoyed her, and I definitely didn't want to do that.

Taking my hand in hers she squeezed it, smiled and said, 'Sure there's nothing to forgive, Bobbie. Come closer to me.'

Handing me a packet of cigarettes she asked me to light two, which I did, while my mind raced to make sense of what had happened.

As that reliable old Ulsterbus chugged its way through the avenue of trees, Downshire loomed large and awesome in the crystal moonlight. Tired patients scrambled down noisy metal steps and were counted once again. Our day trip was over.

'Sister, can .., can I see you again,' I hesitated.

'Aren't you on duty tomorrow?' she asked.

'Yes, I'm not off 'til Friday, I explained.

'I know that. I checked your work rota yesterday,' she said coolly.

'THE ARRANGEMENT'

As time elapsed, Sister O'Flynn's appetite for the unusual bordered on gluttony, which I always believed was one of the seven deadly sins, the others being pride, covetousness, lust, anger, envy and sloth. A rare mixture of emotions would affect most people, at least some time in their lives, and I would be no different.

It was a well known fact in Nursing, at the time, that if you wanted to proposition a woman you did so on a Friday afternoon, when she knew she wasn't working the weekend.

It was on a Friday afternoon such as this, in the Nurses' Canteen, that she set out to further my education once again and, at the same time, really telling me nothing at all.

With a cup of tea in one hand and a cigarette in the other, her main worry in this life seemed to have something to do with her age, which in itself was something I knew nothing whatsoever about.

I believed life was one long adventure, that the energy I possessed at the time was something which God had given me forever.

I had nursed the old and the infirm, and sympathised with their condition should they be bedridden, or just able to hobble about, so you'd think having had experience like that would have given me some insight into the future. But I still believed that infirmity, ill health and having to slow down, would never happen to me. These guys were just plain unlucky!

At twenty-two, I was bouncing, without pain or ache, and, as far as I was concerned, this was the way it was always going to be. No-one had told me otherwise.

'My husband doesn't love me,' said Sister O'Flynn, and she went on to explain that she was forty-five and had missed out a lot in life.

I knew her husband very well and had been drinking with him for a few months. Paddy was full of love. He had treated me to supper in

Rea's Restaurant; bought me Green Chartreuse, when I hadn't the money to buy him one back; helped me to my room in the Nurses' Home, when I was too drunk to make it on my own. Yet here she was, running him down behind his back and trying to convince me he was a bad man, when I knew only too well he was definitely one of the best!

I wasn't going to fall for any shite like this. I didn't know it then, but in later life I was to discover that this was one of the first points in conversation used by many women, who were out for a good time. That simple line, 'My husband doesn't love me any more,' said it all. A statement such as this was akin to using gelignite to open your front door, when a less dramatic entry would suffice.

'I like you very much,' interrupted my pattern of thought, as she gave me one of those baby smiles that I knew to be popular in a business such as this.

Every time she appeared at the tea table, the top three buttons of her Ward Sister's uniform always remained open, revealing heavily stretched sunburned skin, for as far as the eye could see, which in reality wasn't far, but far enough to make you wonder where the white began.

'You make me very happy, Bobbie,' she confided.

'Thank you Sister, you're very welcome,' I answered, thinking if my mother ever taught me anything she taught me good manners. County Fermanagh was Ireland's heartland for good manners and wasn't that where I came from?

Mother would constantly remind me, that 'Good manners were easily carried,' to which my father would add 'Aye, and they cost nothing as well!' I always remembered that.

'Nurse Hanvey, it's like this,' she said sternly, as if trying to shock me back into listening to her again and looking at me clinically, as her outstretched finger brushed the back of my hand, once. She said she would be asking me to do some things for her, and that as I grew older I would learn to appreciate why she had asked for my help that day.

I had been riding her on a daily basis now, for some months, and still I hadn't a clue as to what she was talking about.

'You may or may not enjoy what is going to happen between us, but if you say yes I will help you with your studies. I'll get you old examination papers, and at the end of three years I'll ensure you are a fully qualified Psychiatric Nurse,' she added.

'Fuck me, what a salesman,' I thought. 'Jesus Christ, she must be planning to get me to murder her husband. Oh my good, holy fuck, and him one of the nicest fellas I've ever met. Look at all the cigarettes and whiskey he's given me. I'll be locked up in the Crumlin Road jail for ten lifetimes and I'll never see Maggie again.'

'Nurse Hanvey, are you listening to me?' she demanded, as she inhaled deeper from her new cigarette.

'Yes, Sister, whatever you need,' I gulped.

'It's good I can count on you, Bobbie, but as yet, I cannot say what it is I want you to do for me,' she smiled.

Jesus, she's called me Bobbie again! I wish she'd make up her fuckin' mind.

'You do know where I live; three miles out the Ballybunny Road?' she queried.

'Yes, indeed I do, I know it,' I agreed, at the same time not wanting to offend authority with a smart answer.

'Well, as it happens, Nurse Hanvey, I was looking at your work rota on the notice board today, and I see you're off duty on Monday next. He's working in Belfast on Monday, and won't be home until four o'clock.'

Oh my good God, she had the whole thing figured out; this was definitely going to be murder with a capital M. I'd be killing Paddy around tea time, hardly giving him enough time to take his coat off, put on his slippers, and sit down beside the fire to read the papers.

'I want you at my house at one o'clock,' she insisted.

Unable to take any more of the suspense, and believing I had a right to know what was going to take place, I decided to take the bull by the horns and place my cards firmly on the table.

'Right, Sister, do you want me to poison him, or shoot him?' I demanded, unconsciously raising my voice just that little bit too high.

Suddenly heads, uniforms and chairs were turned and were facing in our direction from various points throughout the canteen. Gazing at us with shocked, disturbed faces that demanded an immediate explanation, they just sat there like stone, and stared. Shrugging my shoulders, I smiled over at them, as if I was only joking, and laughed the whole thing off.

Now the police would have dozens of reliable witnesses. In fact they'd have so many they probably wouldn't even bother to call them all.

'Nurse Hanvey, what the fuck are you talking about?' she snapped, and at the same time speaking low from the corner of her mouth, like an amateur ventriloquist, struck down with the palsy.

'Wise up, you silly, fucking loud-mouthed prick,' she fumed.

'Oh, my good sweet holy fuck,' I thought, 'her language is fuckin' rotten, and she's supposed to be a responsible Ward Sister, always setting a good example to young Student Nurses like me. Some fuckin' Ward Sister this.'

'Look,' she sighed, taking a short, quick pull from a Benson and Hedges, 'all I want you to do is to come to my house for your dinner on Monday. Do you think you can do that much right? Anyway, don't worry, we'll have a nice time,' she laughed as she slid the tall, salt cellar across the table, and into my half open hand. Her laugh bothered me.

'O.K. then, I'll see you on Monday,' I agreed.

'MONTANA MORIARTY'

Getting up early on Monday morning, I shaved, washed and dressed, then threw my dirty clothes into the communal washing machine.

Going down stairs, three steps at a time, I entered the common room, where residents would watch television and relax.

It was completely empty, and I must admit I always liked it that way, because every time I walked on its highly polished, hollow wooden floor, it echoed sharply and deeply, like fresh sods thudding on a coffin lid. This sound gave me the uncomfortable feeling of possessing more authority than I felt I was entitled to.

Such were the simple pleasures of youth, where sounds and smells were appreciated and interpreted to a point well beyond my reason.

Sitting down in the corner armchair, which was my favourite, I turned on the electric fire with the toe of my shoe and, lifting The Irish News, scanned the latest happenings in the world at large, outside the safe perimeter of Downshire Mental Hospital.

Looking out through a wall of windows I could see Maggie's bedroom with the curtains still closed, in the Female Nurses' Home, only thirty yards opposite.

She had been on night duty and probably wasn't long into bed. I remember thinking how she was and of missing her terribly. She was the only true love I had ever known, yet here I was about to start walking in the ice and snow to visit Sister, whom I didn't love, and she knew that, and who didn't love me, and I also knew that, but it didn't seem to make any difference to either of us.

One thing for sure, it wasn't my heart that was making me go there. Maybe it was curiosity, or just simply the anticipation of doing things I hadn't done before.

Coming out through the front door of the Male Home, I bumped into Staff Nurse Moriarty from County Kerry. Because of her massive breasts, the boys had christened her 'Montana', having heard that the mountains were huge in 'The Treasure State'. 'Treasure Chest would be more like it,' I thought.

A recurring joke at the time informed us that if Montana should fall on her face she would strike oil, and those who knew her said she had nipples as big as budgies' heads.

The name 'Montana Moriarty' sure had one hell of a ring to it, and also being heavily into country music she followed 'Big Tom' and his band, 'The Mainliners', to dances all over Ireland. She knew every song he had ever recorded off by heart, and never failed to let us know when he had a new one due for release.

From May 'til late September, when windows in the Nurses' Homes were seldom if ever closed, her record player would be turned up full blast, so that we, too, could enjoy the talents of Ireland's undisputed 'King of Country Music'. Songs such as, 'The Carroll County Accident', 'B.J. the D.J.' and 'The Old Log Cabin for Sale' were played so often I knew them better than she did. I suppose, for that at least, I would be eternally grateful.

The result of her travels following the showbands meant she was off work more times than she attended but, being a brilliant nurse, she was well thought of by the Hospital Administration. They were happy to tolerate her shortcomings, as indeed they did with all of us. She was allowed to do her own thing, and remained a very happy and efficient human being.

That morning when I saw her she was singing loudly and happily at the top of her voice a song which was popular in Ireland at the time.

'Shall I ne'er see you more, gentle mother,
in the fields where the wild flowers grow;
I am sorry for that loss I can't recover,
'Neath yon willow lies my gentle mother low.'

'Good morning, Nurse Moriarty,' I said. 'You're one fine singer.'

'And the top of the morning to ye, Bobbie. Thank you, I can only but do my best,' she replied in her soft Irish brogue.

At that time in mental nursing numerous girls from the Republic of Ireland came North to do their training, and many of them settled in Downshire and the Downpatrick area, after qualifying, only returning to their homes when they died. Few of them ever married, but instead totally devoted their lives to caring for the patients, and in sharp contrast to Ulster girls, they possessed a quality of innocence and deep, religious conviction which was so beautiful it had to be experienced to be believed.

'And how's the world abusing you, Montana?' I asked.

'Sure isn't it abusing everybody, not alone me,' she laughed.

'If you happen to see Maggie, would you tell her I'll see her in the canteen, at tea time?'

'Yes, Bobbie, I'll do that, certainly,' she replied.

The snow was falling faster now bringing with it a silence which suited my own expectant, bewildered mood.

Within the hour I was standing in the welcome warmth of Sister's highly-decorated front room, gazing out onto a living Christmas Card, if ever I'd seen one. Her long white lawn, randomly planted with tall needled fir trees, looked very much at home in this seasonal landscape. Red robins danced and kicked angrily on the fluffy ground. They were confused and baffled as to where all the little worms had gone, and were not at all amused with this new icing on their Christmas cake.

I saw their predicament, and sympathised with them. Their present task was almost an impossible one, and the sorrow I felt brought me in a flash back to my childhood, to the day when I found the wounded frog in our garden.

My Da had said, 'Don't worry son, they eat them in France,' to which I replied loudly, but under my breath, 'Dirty bastards.'

I cried on that day, and when neighbours enquired of my mother as to why I was in such a distressed state, she replied, 'Aw pass no heed on him. Sure wouldn't he cry for the ducks going barefoot!'

Such was the philosophy of life used when growing up in the Brookeborough of the nineteen fifties. This was one of the earliest lessons I ever received in the art of learning to 'paddle my own canoe', and I must admit it was a good one.

The only signs of human habitation out front, were my footprints which began at the base of the heavy mahogany gates, and stopped dead at Sister's front door step. The snow was coming heavier now, and my tracks were being quickly filled in, right before my eyes.

There I was, warmly and safely inside her home without even a trace of my arrival and I remember thinking this was like pure magic: now you see it, now you don't.

Ever since the time I spent in England a few years earlier, rambling round the place and sleeping rough in various accommodations, from miners' security huts to Salvation Army Hostels, and singing in dingy folk clubs, I forever appreciated warm rooms and especially warm rooms which looked out on cold settings such as this.

I never wanted to be cold again.

For some time now, as I was standing there in Sister O'Flynn's living room, I had noticed that the kitchen where she was supposed to be preparing dinner had gone deadly quiet, and I wondered if she was loading the gun for the final showdown - or adding paraquat to the coca cola.

Just as I had finished thinking that, a strained voice, full of authoritative command, gushed out in my direction.

'Nurse Hanvey, come here immediately.'

'Now I'm for it. It's fuckin' me she's going to shoot!' I thought.
I stood rooted in shock and felt the blood draining from my face like
a burst hot water bottle, as snowflakes still putted and melted on the
warm window panes.

'Nurse Hanvey, come right here, when you are fucking called,' she
shouted.

I noticed how she never failed to add the 'g's' to her word endings,
but I still couldn't be convinced, that it sounded any better than fuckin'
without the 'g'.

During my school days in County Fermanagh, my mates would laugh
me to ridicule, and call me a cissy if I ever used a 'g', so for many
years afterwards I fell into line and never used one at all.

They would say it was only Protestants who spoke like that, and the
last thing they wanted was to be mistaken for a Protestant. Starting
to use them later on in life was to become a problem. Sometimes you
managed to get it right and sometimes you didn't. Such was the way
of life in Northern Ireland at the time.

Turning out of the living room, I stepped into the hallway and stopped
abruptly in the darkened kitchen doorway. What I was to see would
have a traumatic affect on me for many years to come, and leave me
in constant wonder as to what really was normal and what was
madness in this life. I thought myself fairly normal, yet here I was in
the midst of abnormality, but prepared to go along with it, which also
made me anything but normal - or did it? I just wasn't so sure.

'Oh my good sweet Jesus would you take a look at that,' I thought.

Standing with her back to a roaring 'Aga', wearing only her nurse's
uniform, which hung open from neck to knees, Sister O'Flynn
revealed heavy breasts and full, round, soft belly. Black nylons and
matching suspender belt completed the effect, with carelessly painted
blood-red lips, and darkened-down eyes thrown in for good
measure.

The air in there was thick with the smell of boiling cabbage and raw whiskey. Three tins of bully-beef were stacked precariously on the cooker's shelf. In her hands she held an expensive cut-glass sugar bowl, reminding me of the way in which a priest might lower a chalice at Mass, and me expecting her to be wielding a double-barrelled shotgun!

Later in life I would learn to understand, and even curiously appreciate, such behaviour, but at twenty-two years old and having just arrived from the 'bogs' of Fermanagh, I looked upon all this theatrical stuff as nothing but a short-cut to the fanny.

There was no tugging at skirts, or pulling of elastic here, no quickness of the hand to deceive the eye. This was definitely the open door.

'Nurse Hanvey, remove your trousers right now,' she commanded.

I took them off slowly, rather than remove them, because I felt an order like 'remove' was anything other than friendly.

Carefully resting the sugar bowl on the table, in ritual fashion, she then lifted a milk bottle from the midst of discarded cabbage leaves, grabbed me by the Willie and doused it all over, until no part remained untouched.

Soon, anxious, flicking fingers were scattering pinches of sparkling white sugar crystals like snow over the fresh sticky fluid.

Quickly kneeling down on the brown oil-cloth, which was speckled with more of the crackling granules, she indicated with a straight, falling finger that I was to kneel also.

'Kneel, Hanvey,' she pointed, now dropping the title of Nurse. The boys in the Nurses' Home often maintained that when women go over forty they like to bark and meow when sexually aroused. I prayed she wouldn't ask me to become involved in this stuff because I was very religious and not a cat or dog - I would remind her of this if I had to. Anyway, I got the clear feeling she didn't like me very much.

Holding out reaching, tacky fingers she took my hands and began to recite a prayer and me being a good Catholic from birth, I automatically joined in without being asked to do so, and without thinking why I was doing it.

'Nurse Hanvey, we are all corrupt and depraved in this life,' she preached. 'We are filled with evil, filled with lust and filled with sin,' to which I interjected, 'And filled with shite as well, Sister.'

She did not like that, she did not like that one little bit.

Going down on all fours, she began licking the milky, sugary mess.

'So much for hygiene and the proper nursing procedure,' I thought. She was now trying to catch it in her mouth, with no hands, again bringing me back to the Halloweens of my childhood, when I'd bob for apples in George Kirk's scullery. Sometimes you caught one, sometimes not.

Her mouth was now quickly filling up, with some stuff sliding from its sugary corners and a look of pure madness in her rolling cataleptic eyes; that beautiful cemented stare of temporary insanity.

Before I had time to save myself she pushed me backwards onto the floor, kissing me hard and at the same time releasing everything she'd taken from me back into my mouth.

'Drink this, take it back you fuckin' bastard, drink it!' she ordered, in a mumbled scream, as she tried to smother me with caked, gooey lips.

She had just dropped her very first 'g', and exposed her true station for the first time.

I said to myself, 'Well fuck me, there's a first time for everything!'

When it was over, she stood as erect as a Ward Sister should, rubbed her lips dry with the back of her hand, dusted her uniform with sticky, flicking fingers and turned her back on me, slowly trying to restore her previous composure of respectability.

'How are your studies coming along, Bobbie?'

'I'm doing the heart and lungs at the moment.'

'Mmm, heart and lungs. Very interesting subjects indeed. I'll get you some good papers on those tomorrow. Are you still seeing Maguire?'

'Yes, I am, every day. She's on night duty and I'm having tea with her shortly.'

'Stay here for your tea and I'll tell my husband you just called in to borrow some books. Go to the bathroom and freshen up and I'll tidy up down here,' she insisted, as she pushed me along the hall, and pointed me in the direction of the landing.

After brushing my teeth and washing the sugar down the sink, I was close to vomiting and repeatedly asked myself why I'd done this. The sin I'd just committed had to be high on the scale of the mortal variety, and the fact that one of the 'biggest' prayers in the Catholic religion had been desecrated in such an irreverent way would only compound my crime in the eyes of God.

This was not me. Yet I had gone along with her, and if pushed on the question, I would have to admit I enjoyed the experience, but only at the time, and definitely not now.

I was feeling all the guilt in the world, the exact amount of guilt which my religion expected me to feel. But surely no amount of genuine prayer would get me out of this one.

If I told the priest in Confession I doubt if he'd believe me, so I'd adopt the safe approach and tell nothing at all. There was no point in me disturbing a decent man like Father Burns, who would never think the same of me again.

Tiptoeing downstairs, I quietly turned the lock and gently closed the front door behind me. Three months was long enough, and I just couldn't take any more.

Running out into the snow, she begged me to stay, as frozen flakes melted and streaked on her still naked breasts, now goosepimpled and angry with the cold.

I kept walking and at the same time telling myself over and over again, not to look back.

When the snows finally melted, even my footprints would be gone.

THE CANTEEN

Maggie was seated in the far right hand corner of the Nurses' Canteen when I went over and joined her. Five or six nursing books were stacked neatly on the table beside her left hand.

'Hi Hanvey, and how was your day?' she enquired softly. She always called me Hanvey, even when telling me she loved me. No one else ever did that and no one ever made it sound so good.

'Oh, I'm not long back from Sister O'Flynn's house. She gave me some of her old biology books,' I replied hurriedly, wanting to kill the conversation as quickly as possible.

'This was known as the lie nearest the truth; the one that's always told,' I said to myself ashamedly.

'A great nurse,' she interrupted respectfully, adding how she had worked in Sister's ward and found her a lovely religious lady who never missed Mass.

Now I was definitely beginning to feel awkward and ill at ease in Maggie's company. She was that special thing, the woman who was, and always would be, my shining star, a symbol of all the things that were good in life, and here I was treating her like a stranger.

Until now, when Maggie and I talked, our conversations had been as free as the wind, without sleight of hand or inhibition, but I was now stuck in a world she had never seen and probably never even imagined existed; the same world which I too believed in, until a few months ago.

'Would you like more tea, Bobbie?' she asked.

'Yes, please,' I answered, but now feeling that I wasn't good enough to even use her name.

In the process of adding some sugar to my tea, as she always did, my fingers touched the spoon, and stopped it, just inches from the cup. 'No, thanks, I don't want any sugar.'

'But you always take sugar, you big eejit you,' she laughed.

'Not any more. I've given it up,' I replied.

'But it's not Lent yet,' she giggled.

'I know, I just gave it up and I don't want it any more,' I said.

I never took sugar after that, and she never even asked me why.

'BILLY AND THE HOLY SISTERS'

Nuns were not a common sight in a mental hospital, so when six of them breezed in and 'floated' across the floor of Ward Forty-Nine and told us they were there as part of their training, the staff were flabbergasted. The sameness of the daily routine being broken, if only temporarily, pleased us and added to our sense of disbelief at having found ourselves in such 'heavenly' company.

As the hems of immaculately tailored garments clipped the highly reflective, machine-polished floor they caused small puffs of dust to rise and swirl against the invading summer sunlight.

As we watched, twelve clattering feet came to a standstill outside the permanently closed door of the Charge Nurse's office.

Tap, tap, tap, knocked the eldest.

'Come in Sisters, I've been expecting you; you're very welcome,' beckoned the 'Charge'.

Each of them immediately and automatically fell into single file and said, 'Thank you,' as they slowly edged past him with heads bowed.

Once again the door closed, and the stout lock turned and clicked.

'Did you see that?' grinned my best mate Billy, as he spun full circle on the 'daggered' toes of his winkle-picker shoes. 'I wouldn't mind a night out with the wee fat one,' he beamed. 'I think she fancies me; did you see the way she looked at me?'

'For Christ's sake Billy stop imaginin' things and show some respect. Here's me thinkin' you're a Prod who doesn't exactly like Catholics and here's you wantin' to jump into bed with one of the Holy Sisters. Stop messin', and catch yourself on before it's too late.'

121

'I wouldn't mind introducin' thon wee one to the 'Drum Major' and givin' her a thump of the skin of the goat, while renderin' a verse or two of our glorious 'Sash',' he leered, in his strong Belfast accent.

Pacing up and down with his left shoulder dropped low, his hands in the flute playing position, and throwing his left foot out a full ninety degrees, he started, 'Da da da, da, da, da, da, da da, and its colours they were fine.'

This was definitely the exact haunch and twist of an Orange flute player alright. The movements forever awkward, but graceful in a menacing sort of way.

'Up Rangers,' he chanted and continued marching round and round in a never-ending circle. 'God bless Her Majesty the Queen, Gusty and the loyal heroes of the U.V.F. and one hundred thousand Orangemen,' he saluted, before snapping to attention and commanding me in a half bark to 'Dis....miss!'

'Billy, wise up. Do you honestly believe she'd look at you twice even if you weren't a Protestant?'

'Robert, old son, they like Protestants alright. They get an even bigger kick from us, because they think they've committed a bigger sin.'

'You're sick in the fuckin' head and whoever filled your head with all that shite is even sicker than you. There's no way she'd even consider goin' out with a wee Orange cunt like you.'

'Shusht,' he signalled, placing a long, first finger across his lips. 'Shusht, they're coming back.'

A mass of blackness approached the frosted glass in the office door, and it flung open

'Good evening, Sisters and youse are very welcome to Male Forty-Nine,' he curtsied, in his broad East Belfast accent, bowing too low for the occasion, and making me think he believed he was in Buckingham Palace.

I must admit though, he delivered his line beautifully and with a certain amount of respect, regardless of the shite that was packing his brain, and had started to 'leak' a few minutes earlier.

'And good afternoon to you, Nurse, and thank you for such a lovely welcome; it's lovely to be here,' replied the eldest, who also happened to be the one he fancied.

Grinning like a Cheshire cat he glanced in my direction, jerked his head sideways and winked with one eye at the same time. He was ecstatic.

'Hypocrite,' I whispered, but just loud enough for only him to hear. 'You're welcome, Sisters,' I said.

'Thank you, too, Nurse.'

The Charge then took them on a guided tour of the ward, showing them various points of interest and introducing them to the patients.

'Good afternoon, Sisters,' I mimicked after they were gone, in a broad Belfast accent, bowing low and backing back like a Chinaman. 'You must be about the worst Protestant I've ever come across, Billy.'

'What the hell do you mean?' he snapped.

'Well, one minute you're wantin' to introduce her to the Drum Major, and the next it's 'Good evening, Sisters'. I wish you'd make your stupid mind up. If your friends in the Orange ever get to hear about this, then your days of marchin' to the 'Field' at Finaghy will be well and truly over. They'll throw you out in disgrace and you'll probably end up joining the military wing of the Legion of Mary.'

'You're not tellin' me now that the Legion of Mary have got a military wing?'

'Did you not know that?' I stirred.

'No, I did not,' he answered abruptly.

'So there y'are now, that's a new one for you to raise at your next Lodge meeting,' I teased.

'Oh,' he replied, pretending not to be interested.

'It's well known in these parts that they do their training in the Mourne Mountains at the weekends,' I assured him.

'You're fuckin' jokin',' he faltered.

'No I'm not; they're trained to kill alright, but very slowly, using a technique that's more horrific than the Chinese Water Torture.'

'And what technique would that be,' he probed.

'They beat you to death with a wet lettuce,' I cheered.

'Hanvey, you're one rotten Fenian bastard,' he raged, as he threw a few friendly punches at my shoulder, which soon hurt like hell.

THE BLOTTER FOR HER EYES

The next day, the good Sisters were dispersed throughout the hospital, taking up their new positions in various wards. My favourite from the word go was Sister Terrifica, at least that's what I christened her on our first day on duty together.

Days soon disappeared into weeks and as her presence moulded into the shifts her mystery heightened, and my interest in her became more intense.

I was forever teasing her how I would one day 'get her out of the habit', but she only replied in all seriousness, 'We'll have to pray together soon, Bobbie.'

My answer was always the same. 'It would be a pleasure to pray with you any time, Sister Terrifica.'

She always laughed at this, making me wonder if she believed I was serious. I thought I was, but sometimes I wasn't so sure.

Nuns, she told me, were taught to avoid having eye contact with others, and when out walking they would look straight ahead at all times. Left and right simply wasn't part of their geography.

At every given opportunity after that I would stare her out for minutes at a time, my own eyes sinking deeper into her own dark, sad pools. Her embarrassment was so visible I could almost touch it. Covered from head to foot in the old 'uniform' of nuns, and with only her face showing, as if in a death-mask, she undoubtedly looked the part of the deeply religious, caring person she was, but her eyes told me something different, although I couldn't figure out exactly what that was. There was a barely controlled wildness about them.

Her eye-brows, like two perfectly drawn arches of soot, were the richest, purest black I had ever seen. The whites of her eyes annoyed me with their brightness, so much so I could never see enough of them.

Full, pale lips cried out for a blood transfusion, or the colour of anything, even lipstick.

In reality, she was a black and white photograph.

On the day when we knelt and prayed together, before one of the patients came into the ward and startled us, I was hypnotised by her pale, almost transparent fingers and by the way her rosary beads hugged them, as if raindrops clinging to a summer rose.

Some weeks later, the ward deserted, we sat by the electric fire. It was early afternoon and the patients were either at Occupational Therapy or the Sugar Bowl.

The floor in the dormitory area was the shiniest in the entire hospital. Rows of neatly made beds lay in wait as small, tidy lockers stood smartly to attention.

Sitting in two very low but comfortable chairs I casually asked her, 'What age are you now Sister?'

'Twenty-seven,' she replied, 'and what age are you?'

'Twenty-four and a half,' I smiled.

'If you had to do it all over again would you still be a nun, or would you have chosen a career in nursing?'

'In the County Sligo where I come from all the girls become either nurses or nuns, or emigrate to England or America. There's no work at home for us. But to answer your question, yes, I'd still be a nun. What would you have been had you not become a Nurse?'

'Well Sister, in the County Fermanagh where I come from all the boys become either nurses or .... nuns. I think I'd have become a nun, Sister.'

She smiled a puzzled smile of disbelief, turning her head from me, as she did.

'Seriously, I'd probably still be working in a factory. I left school at fifteen or rather, the vice-principal, Mr Hughes told me to 'consider' leaving and never to buy a motor-bike. I was never able to figure out exactly what he meant by that,' I confessed.

'Perhaps he thought you'd kill yourself,' she explained.

'You're right. That's exactly what he meant. It's funny, but I never thought of that before.'

'Sure, it's impossible to think of everything Bobbie,' she consoled.

'That's true Sister; that's very true indeed. Do you not become very uncomfortable, especially during the summer, wearing all those clothes?'

'Oh, you mean my habit?' she corrected.

'Yes,' I nodded.

'Yes, it does become extremely hot, but rules are rules,' she emphasised.

'And is your hair very long under your head-dress?' I gestured.

'It almost reaches my waist, but I'm having it cut soon.'

'Will you keep me a little piece when you do?' I asked.

As if speaking her thoughts aloud she whispered, 'God, am I hearing this?' and then softly continued, as her eyes rolled, with some embarrassment, 'We'll see.'

'Sister, can I say something?' I pressed.

'If you must,' she answered, again staring into the cold, grey bars of the turned-off electric fire and adding, 'Sure nothing has stopped you yet!'

'You're very beautiful for a nun,' I ventured.

'And you're extremely ugly for a nurse,' she countered.

'Sure, good looks aren't that important anyway, Sister.'

'You're right, of course they're not,' she smiled trying to lessen my discomfort, which was now causing me to focus on the sparkling chrome, wall-mounted fire.

'Bobbie, always remember the good Lord giveth and the good Lord taketh away, and in your case when he was handing out the good looks he certainly did his fair share of taking away,' she laughed.

'Very, very good Sister,' I dryly stammered and continued gazing at the fire.

My father used to tell me that a favourite traditional Irish pastime was sitting in chairs and gazing or spitting into fires. We were no better than cats, he would say; fascinated with fires. We were fires on the fuckin' brain.

If I had been one hundred per cent sure of not getting electrocuted I'd have turned it on and spat into it, just for badness. My father also insisted that most people who were found dead in chairs in front of fires, probably spat into them minutes before they had passed away, but the only manner of proving that they had actually spat would have been if they'd missed it. My father was some character alright.

Out of the corner of my eye I could see Sister was still smiling and twiddling with her rosary.

'Did you know Bobbie, that the good Lord carries each and every one of us in the palm of His hand, and when someone falls off that's when they die,' she diverted.

'Get away,' I said in disbelief, but also failing to grasp the magnitude of such a theory.

'When you think about it carefully you'll discover it makes sense,' she added.

'Sister, why do you keep looking away?'

'We're not supposed to have eye contact; I told you that earlier,' she explained.

'But we had good eye contact five minutes ago,' I argued. She never answered and kept gazing at the wall.

'I love your eyes so much, little Sister. Can I please look into them just one more time?'

Quickly turning round, she opened her eyes as wide as she possibly could, stretched her skin by pulling a funny face, gaped at me intensely for all of two seconds and glanced away again.

'There you are now, was that alright,' she smiled mischievously in her infectious Southern brogue.

'That's not funny,' I retorted.

'I thought it was very funny,' she laughed. 'Please forgive me for being flippant but something came over me and I just couldn't he... hel... help it,' she giggled, before bursting into an uncontrollable fit of laughter.

Still, it was nice to see her so happy, even though I'd never seen a nun do that before.

In an instant, sadness replaced merriment as her face lowered, and her eyes blankly searched the mirrored shine on peeping shoes.

Delicate fingers which cried out to be touched, fidgeted nervously with the unending span of beads and twisted the chain to breaking point.

It was as if every ounce of energy in her body was trying to escape but had no idea of where to go.

129

Her head slowly arose and the darkest, deepest hovering eyes swung in my direction, met mine, clicked into position and stayed there.

Full, pale, lips revealed a barely visible tremor and prepared to move. This was 'put down' time yet she didn't appear angry, but calm and composed as she'd always been.

'Bobbie, let me put it like this; if I admired men, which I do not, you certainly would not be my first choice of friend,' she said, though not unkindly.

'Jesus, she sure knows how to get even,' I thought.

'But having said that, you are the only person I've ever met who made me feel so good about myself, and treated me as something other than I am. In fact, you make me feel too good about myself; you have begun to make me question my vows. I greatly admire your high spirits and zest for living, but all of this is wrong. I really enjoy your company, but I'm going to request a change of ward so I won't be with you any more,' she concluded.

'Sister, may I now tell you how you make me feel? If it means anything to you, I ....'

'Please tell me,' she interrupted.

'This is going to be difficult, but here goes anyway,' I said, throwing caution well and truly to the wind.

'Go on,' she said, making me feel as if I was isolated and entombed in the silent, black world of the confession box for the first time.

The racing tick of the ward's electric clock unnerved me, compounding my uncertainty.

'Every day and night I think of you, Sister Terrifica. I purposely go to bed to think of you and wonder if all of you is as white as your hands and face. If so, I want to die in your whiteness. Your face looks over me from the darkness and protects me. Your eyes forever cut me like razor blades, without mercy, and I never want them to stop. I want so much to share your loneliness.'

Taking her right hand, which in turn was clutching her rosary, my finger circled her wrist and moved to the inside where her pulse was dancing so fast it was impossible to count the beats.

The blood was gushing in her veins.

Mixed up fingers soon became trapped in the beads and added to her consternation.

'Sister, I long to kiss your skin and hold you and tell you how much I love you. I know it can never happen but at night when I'm alone it does happen.'

Her eyes became blurred as a tiny tear slowly sliced her skin and came to rest on the corner of her mouth.

Removing it with the tip of my finger I tenderly placed it on my tongue.

'Now I carry part of you with me Sister. You taste beautiful.'

Her eyes filled up and became wet and swollen.

As I raised her hand to kiss it she hurriedly jumped from the chair, stepped back from me and cried, 'Stop! Stop! Please stop!'

Turning round she swung right and stormed up the long corridor of echoes with her habit moving as I'd never seen it move before. I heard the familiar jingle of keys and then seconds of silence, as she selected the right one. The heavy lock clicked and the cloakroom door closed solidly behind her, and the lever turned yet again.

A long fifteen minutes passed before the sound of unlocking and locking was repeated. The almost inaudible swish of garments grew louder, and in seconds she was standing over me.

'Please take a seat Sister,' I nodded.

131

'No thank you, I'll stand if you don't mind, and I'll still stand if you do. Bobbie, I must say goodbye,' she said coldly. 'I would like you to have these.'

Her now open, outstretched hand revealed a small rosary with a cross of beautifully cut, sea-green glass, which made the crucifixion almost come alive.

'These touched the image of 'Our Lady of the Americas,' she said 'and will bring you everything that is good and what you wish for in life.'

As they tumbled into my hand her fingers slowly recoiled into her palm and she took one step back.

'Goodbye, Bobbie,' she whispered.

I never answered her or looked up, but instead gazed transfixed at the rosary and repeated the most beautiful sounding name I'd ever heard, 'Our Lady of the Americas.'

Carefully dropping them into the top pocket of my white coat, and throwing my feet up onto the electric fire, I tried to convince myself that the last hour had actually happened.

The next day she was transferred at her own request to another ward, and didn't return to Male Forty-Nine. After that, I often saw her walking and praying in the grounds and sometimes in the canteen, but we never spoke.

I told myself this was a big sin and they didn't come much bigger than this. In fact this was possibly the worst I'd ever committed, but I felt at the same time I'd really done nothing at all.

An old fire and brimstone preacher who came to our annual mission in Brookeborough when I was nine or ten, told us it was possible to commit a mortal sin by just sitting in a chair and thinking 'bad' thoughts. He said you could be blindfolded, bound hand and foot, gagged, ear-plugged and tied in chains, and still be able to commit a mortal sin, so on this occasion, at least, I felt I fitted into that category.

But, I wanted so much to share her loneliness, and was fully prepared to face the everlasting flames of hell just to hold her close. I wanted to be the blotter for her eyes.

THE VISITOR

Some time later I was on night duty, going to bed around eight o'clock in the morning and getting up about four in the afternoon. It was the middle of winter and strangely enough almost on the doorstep of Christmas once again.

Something stirred me and I woke. Trying desperately to focus, my eyes struggled, gazing in total bewilderment through the open, blue door, onto the narrow, dark landing, which was poorly lit from the tired glow of a bare sixty watt bulb.

It was one of those landings which had been painted so many times that the walls had gained a texture all of their own. Purple was the latest addition, being a popular colour at the time. Everything was covered in it, but I still loved that battered, dying, old flat. It was home.

In awe, I stared in disbelief, not knowing exactly where I was, or what she was doing there. It was as if I was the only witness in the whole world to this rare, beautiful vision - my everlasting photograph of unending mystery.

A long, black habit revealed only the shining tips of two resting shoes. Gaunt and ghostly, but in a way which caused no dismay, she calmed my initial shock like an anaesthetic, making me feel no need to panic and content at being covered by her stillness.

Desolate, never-blinking eyes caught the light from the sixty watt and hurled it through the darkness in my direction, sending messages which stirred me from head to foot.

A heavy silver and black crucifix which was jammed at an angle like a six-gun, behind her broad, brown belt occasionally glinted as if trying to sedate me.

Her hands were hidden up opposite sleeves.

My hand moved quietly under the blankets as her eyes were glued on mine. Fixed in the hypnotic stare of death they held me spellbound from a distance of some ten to twelve feet.

Then I heard it! The thump, thump, thump of hurried footsteps running up the creaky old stairs.

My hands quickly abandoned the stored warmth of the bed-clothes and met the cold, winter air of the chilled room for the first time in eight hours. The old 'dinged' alarm clock said, 'Ten to four.'

I signalled with great urgency to warn her of coming danger but as if in a trance she stood statue-like, never flinching or batting an eyelid.

Her long, silent rosary hung motionless by her side.

Suddenly a voice cried out, 'How did you get in here? Who let you in? Get out! Get out! Who do you think you are? Get out! You're not wanted here!'

Her eyes remained fixed on mine as if eating the last meal they would ever see. She never spoke or made a sound.

Then, in complete silence, she slowly turned and was gone.

I never saw her again.

Later that evening I asked the residents of the flats, who had the noses of bloodhounds, if they'd seen her.

They said, 'No one had called who fitted that description.'

But I still wasn't so sure.

'THAT STORMY NIGHT'

I pulled the big, heavy door of Finneston House behind me, locked it, checked it, and stepped out into the driving rain. My late shift was over.

It had been a long, hard day with most of the patients suffering from rampant diarrhoea, having to be bathed and changed over and over again.

Old Percy had broken all previous records, having been washed nine times. He emphatically denied having the runs in the first place, and kept insisting it was only sweat, which had been brought about because the ward temperature 'had been turned up too far.'

'Turn it off, Nurse. Aw, turn it off now,' he pleaded.

After lowering him down for the ninth time into his final soak in Savlon I felt like agreeing with him, and almost believed the heating system could be faulty, which of course it wasn't.

I was jet-lagged, yet I hadn't flown an inch.

Still, a good night's sleep would recharge the batteries and prepare me for more of the same tomorrow, the day after, and the day after that, because the bug which caused so much destruction and dehydration in the old people usually stayed with them for three or four days at a time. There was still much work to be done.

Walking down the path from Finneston with the wind trying its best to turn me inside out, my hands fought with the hood of my anorak as I finally managed to pull it over my head, tie the toggles and, only just, keep on the move.

It was one of those knee-length khaki coats which were popular during the sixties. Far from being waterproof, it gained weight by the second and never failed to flood the corridor in the Male Nurses' Home, whenever I hung it behind the Sluice Room door. It was hopeless, but at ten pounds a bargain in its day.

I hated wearing it at any time, but more especially on rainy days, when I always envisaged being attacked and torn to pieces by a pack of mad dogs. In dry weather the circular strip of fur which decorated the front of the hood looked attractive, in a funny sort of way, but when wet it reeked of rabbit, making me constantly wonder how the manufacturers ever managed to overlook such an obvious health hazard.

The wind whined and mimicked the lonely cries of a sick child as Maggie's voice tried to reach me, only to be blown back again, and scattered into the night. Then a gentle hand rested on my shoulder.

'So you've had a rough day too, Hanvey.'

'Aye, indeed I did. It was diarrhoea all the way, an' I'm totally and utterly exhausted. I just can't wait 'til my head hits the pillow.'

'It was the same in our ward. I've never seen it so bad. There'll be no peace for anyone on duty tonight,' she said wearily.

'It's always worse at night,' I agreed. 'And if someone happens to die before morning it will be plain blue murder in there. They'll have to pull in extra staff. Maguire, I love you so much.'

'I love you too, Hanvey.'

We stopped walking and I kissed her, as the wind pushed and pulled and shoved, and did its best to drive us apart.

She was beautiful, and I told her so.

'Did you hear Nurse Flaherty's getting married soon?'

'To Billy?' I asked.

'Yes, they're a great couple; so well matched. I'm sure they'll be very happy together.'

'Just like us,' I smiled.

'Just like us, Bobbie Hanvey.'
'I want to hold you Maggie. I just want to hold you for the rest of my life.'

'Do you not think your arms would get sore,' she teased.

'I'd hold you 'til my arms dropped off,' I replied.

'And then, Hanvey, how would you hold me?'

'Well that's a good question,' I thought, as I fought for time to think of an answer. 'I'd - I'd, hold you with my head,' I ventured.

'Aye, and it's big enough, that's for sure. Give me a kiss you big eejit ye,' she smiled, as her wet hands touched my face and gently pulled me to her.

'It'll soon be that time of year once again, Maggie.'

'I love Christmas. Are you going to Midnight Mass?'

'Only if you're going,' I emphasised.

'We'll go together and we'll get dressed up,' she enthused.

'But we always dress up for Mass,' I replied.

'I know we always dress up for Mass, Hanvey, but we'll make a special effort just for Christmas.'

The talk of Christmas and Midnight Mass released a happiness from deep within her that I had never witnessed before. It was beautiful. She loved her religion with a passion, and in doing so, she loved and enjoyed life more.

'Everyone needs a focal point in their week,' she would say, 'And Sunday is that special day, and without it every day is just the same.'

'One thing's for sure, there'll be no Connemara or Fermanagh for us this Christmas,' I said. 'I'm on duty. I've been asked to sing at a lot of ward parties so there'll not be much real work done.'
'I'm on duty too. Will you be singing at our party?' she asked.

'I will indeed. I hope you're there when I come over.'

Gently squeezing my hand, she replied, 'I hope so too.'

'I hate staying in the Female Home at Christmas. It's like a morgue when everyone's away home with their families.'

'You could always come to some of the parties with me. It would help pass the time, and sure you could always sing an ould song or two!'

'I'd love to Hanvey, if you don't mind, but there's one thing, I'll not be singing any songs.'

'Don't worry Maggie; we'll have a lovely Christmas.'

Crossing the road, we fought our way to the small green door in the high, ivy-covered perimeter wall which reflected every bit of light it could find. Little heart-shaped leaves twitched and flickered.

It was as if the wall was moving, as we took careful aim with our shoulders and forced the small door back and jumped in, just before the wind slammed it angrily behind us, and then roared over our heads, from above.

Soaked to the skin, her uniform changed colour right before my eyes, from light to royal blue.

Wet, rain-lashed hands caressed my face and diluted salt as my broken whispers of sorry were heard over and over again, and then her shaking words of comfort would spill all over me; 'I'm sorry too; I'm sorry too.'

Dry matches scraped hopelessly on the damp sandpaper edge of a soggy matchbox, and were quickly discarded until there was only one left.

The tall, frightened trees to the front of Downshire were even more scary on a night such as this. How they moaned and creaked, as rain-clad winds tore up the hill and over neatly kept lawns, before smashing their winter's load onto the countless window panes of a million sorrows.

Huddled on hunkers under her long, navy blue cloak we were drenched, but warm and happy in this new castle of ours. Even though the Nurses' Homes were within vision, only fifty yards away, we were for staying put, in the trees.

Male Nurses were not allowed in the rooms of Female Nurses. Female Nurses were not allowed in the rooms of Male Nurses. This was the Hospital policy and to break it would have meant instant dismissal. So although the two homes were only thirty yards apart and we could wave to each other from our windows, or 'phone each other across, this was as far as it was supposed to go.

Many staff broke the rules; Maggie did not.

'A half crown will do it,' she said, out of the blue.

'Jesus,' I thought. 'Will do what?'

'Right; we have only one match left, and if we strike it on the rough edge of a half crown it should light, and then we can have a wee smoke.'

'Now that's brilliant thinking,' I thought.

Timing was of the utmost importance.

She put a cigarette in my lips, and then her own, and waited with quiet anticipation.

Holding the coin tightly between her finger and thumb, I took the last match from the box, and on the second attempt it flared. Her eyes smiled at me as I raised the flame and watched the tobacco change colour, and finally glow into a perfect red, circular dot.

The bright, scarlet lining of her nurse's cloak encased us like a womb, making us more warm and secure than we'd ever thought possible. We were content there, as Joe Dolan probably played a distant dance hall somewhere in the murky bogs of Ireland, and as evil men in back rooms, with murder in mind, drew up plans for twenty-five years of bloody slaughter.
These things were close to us, perhaps as close as twenty miles away, but we didn't know and cared even less.

She never spoke about politics. The happy times were all that mattered. Her father being a fisherman meant he was always concerned with fighting the sea to earn his daily bread. His job commanded him to face the sea and what was happening inland was just never that important.

Like her father, Maggie always faced the sea.

She was the young Student Nurse still at odds with the sixties, who refused to fall into line with the new 'freedoms' which had reached our country for the first time. Some said these new freedoms had come from America, but hundreds of years of the old Catholic ways were still firmly lodged in her brain, like countless splinters of fine jagged glass, each with a word written on it - words never to be used or tested.

Pluck out any of these deadly messages at your peril, and you immediately bled to death and drowned, in thick, swirling rivers of blood.

In turn, my mind was overflowing with pictures of history and religion which were always intermingled and confused, but fully accepted just the same - vivid scenes of lonely Mass Rocks with cowering congregations hiding as resplendent Redcoats on prancing horses approached from the valley - Midnight Mass with the sweet, hypnotic smell of slow, swinging thuribles packed with the smoking incense

141

of Benediction - Rosary beads - happy carefree days as an altar boy; endless guilt from breaking my Confirmation pledge at the age of ten, and of stealing the same cider from the backyard of a neighbour's pub - the bedside, mumbling murmur of death prayers - the pure, white immaculate vestments of the Parish Priest. He, my mother said, 'had the power to turn sinners like me into a pillar of salt in an instant.' So if Maggie Maguire refused to allow me to make love to her, I would understand immediately.

We had been taught an identical doctrine by men and women, all priests and nuns who forever told the same identical story.

It never changed, not even for a moment. In Dublin, Cork or Belfast, or in the jungles of darkest Africa, the same story was being told. This was our story; we were part of the story; in fact we were the story.

Maggie lived that story each and every day.

She never missed Mass and made sure I didn't either.

She learned, believed and saw it through, but I wanted to be different. I thought I could change it and add my own words, but all this had been tried before and never stood the test of time.

Words flew past my ears like silent screams on scissors as her long eyelashes froze in time, revealing sad, stunned circles of disbelief and despair.

The skirt of her uniform was culled and tugged as her body turned in boxer fashion, head low to the waist, bobbing and weaving, but strangely remaining on the same spot and always keeping me at a safe distance. It reminded me of the first time in Finneston House when our hand-shake lasted a life-time, but all too short.

Open fingers fended off unattractive advances as the pounding rain ate our skin and spattered our vision.

The clenched fist she did not know.

The piercing cries of legions of lost souls condemned to madness in drably painted rooms exploded simultaneously in my head, and pleaded hopelessly for me to stop, as the dead generations turned their heads in disgust and continued marching.

I was not what I seemed to be, or what I pretended to be, or even who I thought I was.

For a while, I was what I felt I wanted to be, only it wasn't me. I was so like her. I was basically good, but that was something I could never admit to myself. My heart simply wasn't with me this time. Lips tried to move and form new words of hope, but were paralysed. Our mouths parched, dry and finished.

Fixed eyes waited anxiously for responses which never came.

It would be easy to patch things up. No great harm had been done, but I was somewhere low down on the graph of evolution. I could walk on the ground, but in reality it was only an illusion.

Her eyes died on me, as the sparkle of happiness once within them was snuffed out, as a blessed candle was after Mass - that clearly defined, curling trickle of smoke, bending and wafting beautifully, but soon to disappear.

The memory of taking her on that old Ulsterbus to meet my father and mother all seemed so distant now, and the thought of how happy she looked when I shook hands with her parents for the first time in their West of Ireland home made me wonder what was happening to me. Our hearts had burst with excitement as she raced me the two hundred yards down the long, cobble-stoned jetty to the wheelhouse of her father's boat, where the instruments gleamed and shone like diamonds; then inside to gaze through the little, red cabin window out onto the wild Atlantic. That was my most special present, the thought of which would stay with me forever. Heaven would never come much closer than that.

And now it was over.

Many years later, and not so very long ago, our paths accidentally crossed for the first time since that night when the wind shed tears.

The place, was Mullingar, County West Meath. I had been down there taking photographs of J. P. Donleavy and, on the way home, called into a shop for some cigarettes.

Our Christian names, Maggie and Bobbie were used only once. There was no bullshit.

There was no, 'You're looking great!'

There was no, 'You haven't changed a bit!'

We were never into that stuff. We were so nervous with each other, we didn't know which way to turn.

This time, no Rosary beads fell from trouser pockets to keep conversation on flow, or no stones to be kicked with shining shoes.

No beds lay in the shadows or locker in yellow, half light, to create moods beyond imagination.

It was the other side of a lifetime, and I was on my own.

I spoke to her, and she to me, only I couldn't hear her words any more.

Frantically, I tried to grasp one or two, but they dissolved in mid-air.

Customers passed us by as travellers might at an airport, coming and going from every direction and none, hemming us in and adding to our confusion.

Sentiments were banished from thought as we both failed to admit as to how it used to be. I wanted to apologise and give reasons, but they never came. Our reactions to that chance encounter were identical - complicated, bizarre and hazed, far beyond the point of reason. We were both in this thing together, whatever it was, and we wanted to run away.

But one thing which I did vividly remember and will never forget, was her quiet, dignified, barely concealed hatred for me. It would prove to be the strongest and most sustainable that I would ever encounter.

There was no exchange of addresses, or photographs or telephone numbers, and we parted as we had first met, all those years ago when coming off duty - as strangers.

Her two children were beautiful.

'THE DREAM'

Having neglected my religion for many years, I was amazed at how my mind had stored the faith of my childhood, a faith I thought I'd forgotten, until I dreamt.

A recurring dream I had of my own death should have been a frightening experience, but wasn't. Like a re-run of an old movie, it never changed, and continually showed the conflict and turmoil within me, as I struggled to speak her name for the last time.

Stout, big-breasted women, with ruddy complexions, strong arms and lost opportunities, long since impervious to their husbands' drinking and pawing were now towering over me and collectively gathered round my bedside, as good caring members of the local branch of The Legion of Mary.

So relieved, at being away, even temporarily, from the sickly rush of their partners' breath, they never noticed the cloud of approaching death, which was already surrounding them.

Burning candles helped to purify putrid air, as decade after decade of the rosary was whispered in murmurs, in respect for the last of the human senses to fade.

Prayers of every description, most of them known to me, were repeated furiously, but now and again, a special one, which I'd never heard before, was driven at urgent speed in my direction. These were the heavyweights, the priest had given them just for the night, to be returned by daybreak, when it was all over.

These special prayers would add weight to last minute efforts, in agreeing a plea bargain with the Almighty, in order to get 'this old sinner' a reprieve from Hell, or at the very least a short term in Purgatory - probably ten to fifteen years, if successful!

It was known as the place for lost souls, where the fire was just as hot as the one in Hell, but after doing your time there you were released, so there was light at the end of the tunnel.

It had a fairly good reputation, and I was never frightened of being sent there.

I always believed that going to Heaven would be wonderful, but it always gave me one very serious worry - the finality of it all! After Heaven, there would be no more places to go. No more travelling; rambling or magical mystery tours. Once you were fortunate enough to get there it was, quite definitely, the end of the road.

Curious, shifting shadows quivered, on low praying faces, with erect arms clutching busy Rosary beads, as tired elbows rested on the brilliant white sheets, so lovingly arranged on my bed.

From one time to the next they would be respectfully wrapped in brown, greaseproof paper, and stored in dark drawers, where the light of day could never touch them, usually in the bottom of a wardrobe, and below pyjamas, which were only taken out in times of sickness.

I could recall from my nursing days, that most patients died between five and seven in the morning when the body was at its lowest point of resistance. This, too, would be my time.

I tried to smile, but the little veins and arteries were saying they couldn't keep me going for much longer. They were becoming blocked, broken and hopeless, and I slipped out of consciousness for a few seconds.

On coming round again, the whisper of praying voices had changed to a constant, purring drone. The same sound made by the air conditioning in Finneston House when I first met Maggie all those years ago.

Then for no apparent reason, things became so clear and sharp again.

Cotton-wool buds, loaded with freshly diluted Savlon, were peeling through layers of caked, foul-smelling mucus on parched lips, now trembling and useless. But those same lips, had nevertheless, tasted the fresh sweetness of her summer breath, back in the days, when all this old dying 'stuff', was never even contemplated.

In the next room, just beyond the prayers, relations gathered for the waiting.

Prim, straight-laced ladies who nodded more often than they spoke, and all wearing those bee-hive hats, sat with poker straight backs, constantly adjusting hemlines, that one quarter of an inch or so, to ensure respectability, and at the same time quickly eyeing the menfolk, to see if they'd noticed the difference.

It was in places like these that 'matches' were made.

My eyes, sunken and starry now, saw nothing, as a lonely tear slowly escaped, and made its last, long journey down the side of my face, at the same time, cutting a cool, refreshing swathe through the thick pallored sweat of death.

A hundred voices, in perfect unison, began to recite The Rosary, led by those good women in the front. Those good women of The Legion of Mary very soon would leave the house, and walk or drive to their own homes, where their husbands would enquire as to why they'd stayed so long. They would ask the names of the menfolk at 'the wake', just to check the presence of randiness, on a scale of one to ten, of the entire assembly. That would, or would not, help to instil some 'peace of mind'.

Very soon, those holy women would return to the smell of stale Guinness and last minute orders in the bedroom. They would once again pretend, by saying the right words at the right time, and sigh and moan on cue, as the husbands drove it home, calling them names they didn't know on their wedding day.

Life sure was one funny old excursion, but 'my bus' was pulling up to 'the terminal' for the last time.

The frantic rubbing of my hands slowly changed to a touch so gentle I wondered who on earth it could be.

'Could it be her?'

No, there would be no possibility of that; that was too long ago. That was at the other end of a lifetime.

Any minute now, rosary beads would be dropped back into pockets, prayer books carefully placed in handbags and candles blown out.

Sheets would be draped over mirrors in the battle against evil and clocks stopped at the exact moment of my departure.

Aerosols of captured fragrance, stolen from the lilac, pine and every other flower and tree in the forest, would be hissed around the room before the breeze from open windows gradually diluted the 'mix' and restored a healthy 'normal' freshness once again.

Then the holy water rained over me, so gentle and welcome, like a summer shower, cooling me for the longest journey I would ever take.

EPILOGUE: 'WHERE ARE YOU GOING SIR?'

A couple of hundred yards down the road in front of me, below the tall trees, the hustling bustle in the moon-lit darkness left me in no doubt that I was about to confront another one.

As my old Ford car stumbled nervously towards it, blackened shapes of busyness scurried and stopped. Like a swarm of fireflies, jumpy cigarette tips glowed, glided, swooped and disappeared again. This was it!

The big road-block was getting closer and loomed directly across my path. Having braked early to minimise the sound of the grinding of metal on metal, I was now fully prepared to splash out and invest in new pads, and at the same time hoped my discs hadn't suffered too much damage.

The grinding always seemed louder at times such as this, causing me to grit whatever few teeth I had and screw my face up. Jesus! How I hated noisy brakes.

Verey-lights lit up the dying summer sky and revealed countless white eyes peering out of greased-up skulls. Warm rain pounded and bounced on the shining barrels of ever-ready guns and two brown, well-stoned land-rovers parked deliberately told me it was definitely time to stop.

A young U.D.R. soldier's torch peered through a thousand, red rain drops as I pushed the button, causing the glass between us to disappear somewhere down into the middle of the door.

'Some brakes you've got there, Sir,' he grinned.

'What brakes?' I answered, letting him know I knew I hadn't got any.

'Now, now Sir, there's no need to get touchy. I think it would be a good idea to get them fixed.'

'You're not going to believe this,' I said, 'But on approaching your road-block I said to myself, because I hate to hear the grinding, it annoys my head, that it was time to have them replaced. I'll do it tomorrow,' I assured him.

'Now you're talking Sir. That's the job.'

'You're not going to do me, then?' I asked.

'We've more to do than do people for bad brakes. That's a job for the police. What we're more interested in is helping to keep Ulster free from terrorism, so that decent folk can be left alone.'

His line was straight from an old U.D.R. television recruitment advertisement, popular during the nineteen seventies, which showed a very irate man having his car searched at a road-block.

'Why don't you go and catch some terrorists,' he had said to the soldier, 'And lave dacent folk alone.'

Then, I noticed his attitude harden slightly as he reminded me it was 0200 hours, or in layman's lingo, as he also put it, two o'clock in the morning.

'Now, Sir, would you mind telling me what all this gear's doing in the back seat of your car?'

'They're my cameras. I'm a photographer.'

'Aye, I see that. You must be expecting World War Three,' he grinned. 'You've the best of good gear here. One, two, three, Hasselblad cameras and a stack of lenses. Must have cost you a fortune,' he mumbled as his flash lamp continued its search.

'Indeed they did and I'm still paying for them. Did you know that N.A.S.A. uses Hasselblads and there's two lying on the moon?' I asked.

'I know that. My best mate has one, but he's only got the standard lens. Best camera in the world,' he pronounced.

'I can second that,' I agreed.

'Would you mind stepping out of the vehicle and opening your bonnet and boot, Sir?'

'O.K.,' I answered, as he opened the door and gestured for me to get out.

'Why doesn't the Government supply these soldiers with umbrellas?' I asked myself. 'I'll get soaked.'

I stepped from the vehicle and the rain and wind whacked me like a punch-ball, as the young soldier led me in the direction of my own bonnet - and before you could say, 'Jesus, what a night,' the white narrow beam of his torch was dancing on plug leads, wires, engine and radiator, until he was well satisfied there was nothing lurking there that shouldn't. A slam of the bonnet, and it was on to the boot.

The expression, 'Aye, aye and what have we got here then,' always reminded me of the times when I used to watch 'Dixon of Dock Green' on TV every Saturday evening, only this guy was a million miles removed from old Dixon.

'They're portable flash units,' I explained, hoping he wouldn't lift the blanket behind them and find the six bottles of poteen underneath.

'Portable flash guns,' he repeated. 'What's that red thing and look this one's blue and this one's orange?'

'They're coloured filters. I can change the colour of the forest with them. I can make trees red and the grass orange, and people blue.'

'True Blues, I hope,' he laughed. 'I think turning the grass orange is a great idea, but why do you want to turn the trees red?'

'Just for special effects,' I shrugged. By this stage, I was soaked to the skin and dreaded getting back into the car.

Having bought brand new seat covers I realised the amount of water my clothes were carrying would do them no good whatsoever.

Clunking the boot closed and, thank God, never noticing the poteen, he asked me to get back into the vehicle again and I did.

Leaning through the open window he shone the light which had changed to red again, into my eyes, nose and tonsils.

'Jesus, I hope that red light doesn't make my eyes look blood-shot or he'll do me for drunken driving,' I thought desperately.

'Now Sir,' he directed, in a manner which he hadn't used before, 'Where the fuck are you going to at 0200 hours with a car load of cameras?'

'I'm going to take a photograph,' I said lamely, at the same time wishing I was at home fast asleep in my warm bed.

A black soldier, the first black soldier I'd ever seen in the U.D.R., walked and then reversed and turned and turned again in the way soldiers do in the daylight, right up to the car.

'Everything all right, Sarge?' he enquired, in a broad Belfast accent.

I couldn't believe it ....

'Fine, Billy. Just fine,' answered the Sarge.

'Well if it isn't Nelson Mandela,' I thought, 'And he called him Billy! Enough to make King William turn in his grave.'

'You tell me you're going to take a photograph. Where?' he demanded.

'Tullymore Forest Park,' I said.

'Now let me get this right. You tell me you're goin' to Tullymore Forest Park, where the Mountains of Mourne sweep down to the sea, at 0200 hours to take a photograph with a car load of cameras?'

'I am indeed,' I smiled.

With his patience well and truly tested, and almost at breaking point, he stuck his head further though the window until our faces were only inches apart.

Almost at the end of his tether he asked steadily, 'You're going to Tullymore Forest to take a photo of what?'

'Of an owl,' I quipped.

'What sort of an owl is it,' he persisted.

'An oul' whore,' I guffawed.

Tossing his heavy SA80 rifle onto the roof of the car he fell to his knees roaring with laughter, his loud bellows being interspersed with words such as 'Jesus,' - 'Holy Fuck,' and 'The bastard!'

Suddenly, ten or twelve of his comrades flew out of the hedges and from below land-rovers and an orchestra of ringing, metallic clicks convinced me my number could very well be up.

A dozen or more rifles were pointed in my direction, from every angle on the road-block, but the laughing continued from the ground below.

'Are you alright, Sarge?' shouted 'Nelson Mandela'.

'That —, that —, that fucker's goin' to take a photograph of an owl,' he quavered.

'What sort of owl is it, Sarge?' snapped 'Nelson'.

'An oul' whore,' said the Sarge laughing again.

The entire platoon went into hysterics as two squaddies lifted their leader to his feet while 'Nelson' danced and cheered on the road.

'I knew it,' twigged the Sarge. 'You're Hanvey, aren't you?'

'Hanvey, Bobbie Hanvey.' - 'Bond, James Bond!' I imagined.

'You used to work in The Mental, isn't that right?'

'I did. I left it in 1973.'

'You'd have known my father then. Billy Baxter.'

'Charge Nurse Baxter! You're joking. I knew him very well. He was very good to me when I was there,' I said in utter disbelief.

'Well, he died last week,' replied the young soldier.

'I'm really very sorry to hear that. He was so good to me.'

Charge Nurse Billy Baxter was an Ulster Protestant in every sense of the word: A Sunday church goer who didn't drink, smoke or use bad language. Billy's motto in life was 'Live and let live'. When certain nurses from my own religion constantly lambasted and tried to embarrass me in front of Protestant staff for being in the Civil Rights Movement, Billy treated me as one of his friends - to him our differences were unimportant.

This young soldier was a son of his father's, alright.

'I'm sure you miss him a lot,' I said, and meant it.

'Aye, that I do indeed. But that's life. I often heard him talking about you when I was small, and the antics you used to get up to in Downshire. So away you go young Hanvey, and mind yourself when you meet up with the owl.'

'I will. Goodnight and thank you.'

As I drove away from that drab but most friendly of road-blocks the young soldier's silhouette gradually grew smaller in the wing-mirror until it finally was no more.

Then my mind began to wander back to that dark, December day in 1966 when I first started working in Downshire.

The memories kept flooding back and would visit me forever.